LIVING PRAISE

To order additional copies of *Living Praise,* by Allan R. Handysides,
call 1-800-765-6955.

Visit us at www.reviewandherald.com for information on other
Review and Herald® products.

A
SOUND
MIND

A
HEALTHY
BODY

A
GRATEFUL
HEART

Living Praise

ALLAN R. HANDYSIDES

REVIEW AND HERALD® PUBLISHING ASSOCIATION
Since 1861 | www.reviewandherald.com

Review and Herald® titles may be purchased in bulk for educational, business, fund-raising, or sales promotional use. For information, e-mail SpecialMarkets@reviewandherald.com.

The Review and Herald® Publishing Association publishes biblically based materials for spiritual, physical, and mental growth and Christian discipleship.

The author assumes full responsibility for the accuracy of all facts and quotations as cited in this book.

Unless otherwise noted, all texts are from the New King James Version. Copyright © 1979, 1980, 1982 by Thomas Nelson, Inc. Used by permission. All rights reserved.

Scripture quotations marked NASB are from the *New American Standard Bible,* copyright © 1960, 1962, 1963, 1968, 1971, 1972, 1973, 1975, 1977, 1994 by the Lockman Foundation. Used by permission.

Texts credited to NIV are from the *Holy Bible, New International Version.* Copyright © 1973, 1978, 1984, International Bible Society. Used by permission of Zondervan Bible Publishers.

This book was
Edited by Penny Estes Wheeler
Copyedited by James R. Hoffer
Designed by Trent Truman
Cover photo © iStockphoto.com / jpmediainc
Typeset: Bembo 11/13

PRINTED IN U.S.A.
13 12 11 10 09   5 4 3 2 1

Library of Congress Cataloging-in-Publication Data
Handysides, Allan, 1941-   .
   Living praise : a sound mind, a healthy body, a grateful heart / Allan Handysides.
      p. cm.
 1. Seventh-day Adventists—Doctrines. 2. Christian life—Seventh-day Adventist authors.
3. Health—Religious aspects—Seventh-day Adventists. I. Title.
   BX6154.H2973 2009
   248.4'86732--dc22

                         2009022981

ISBN 978-0-8280-2497-6

DEDICATION

To Elder Jan and Kari Paulsen,
supporters and encouragers of health ministry over the past 10 years
in promulgating our message of the Adventist lifestyle.

ACKNOWLEDGEMENTS

Kathleen Kuntaraf, M.D., MPH, is an associate director of the Health Ministries Department of the General Conference of Seventh-day Adventists. She works with youth to prevent at-risk behavior and promotes the Youth Alive program to build resiliency in children. She previously served as the ADRA director for the Far Eastern Division and the Health Ministries director for the Southern Asia-Pacific Division.

Peter Landless, M.B., B.Ch., M.Med, FCP(SA), FACC, is the executive director of the International Commission for the Prevention of Alcoholism and Drug Dependency, a United Nations chartered organization promoting abstinence from harmful substances. His specialty is internal medicine and cardiology, and he is an ordained minister of the Seventh-day Adventist Church.

Stoy Proctor, M.Div., MPH, is a nutritionist, the author of "Breathe-Free: The Plan to Stop Smoking," and an ordained minister of the Seventh-day Adventist Church. He has been involved in active leadership in health ministry for more than 20 years and currently chairs the General Conference Nutrition Council.

The late Thomas Zirkle, M.D., FACS, was a plastic surgeon and served as an associate director of the Health Ministries Department of the General Conference of Seventh-day Adventists. He worked at Loma Linda University for many years and played a key role in the development of the Sir Run Run Shaw Hospital, located in Hangzhou, Zhejiang Province, People's Republic of China.

CONTENTS

INTRODUCTION

This little book outlines a set of concepts that can lead you to a longer and happier life. People often think of health as being achieved only by following strenuous adherence to rules and regulations, but we believe that the basis of health rests—not in us—but in the gift of life given as part of God's grace. Our response to the gift is important insofar as we cherish the health we have been given, whether in a bountiful or limited amount. Gratitude gives a mind-set that seeks a relationship with God, the Life-giver. Dogged pursuit of health without full attention to the gracious aspects of compassion and caring does little good.

Few of us can attain fullness of health and wholeness unless we learn to love. To love God, to love ourselves, and to love other people as much as we love ourselves—this should be our whole pursuit because it yields contentment on so many fronts.

When the November 2005, *National Geographic* explored the "Secrets of Living Longer," Dan Buettner identified Seventh-day Adventists as one of the groups who live the longest. This book outlines the basics of the Adventist lifestyle and thus unlocks the "secrets" to living a long and rich life.

Living Praise is not a theological treatise, nor is it a scientific review. Its goal is simply to bring to the reader a concept of wholeness that is fundamentally sound in Christian belief and scientific backing.

The concepts in this book are not original, as they are culled from many sources, but they are expressed in a format that emphasizes the pleasure and joy of gratitude. We call this the Celebrations of Health.

I am responsible for this book, and all its mistakes, but wish to acknowledge the massive input of my colleagues in the Health Ministries Department of the General Conference. I cannot fail to mention how much I appreciate the hard work of my assistant, Elizabeth Pettit, who has typed, retyped, and corrected so many of these pages. She has been invaluable.

I am not an English major, as you will no doubt recognize; the anecdotal illustrations are an attempt to facilitate your reading, not to substantiate any science to which I have alluded.

The publishing house and its editors have edited the text and provided illustrations. I wish to thank them for their patience—which I no doubt stretched to the fullest.

Meeting the deadlines while meeting my multiple other obligations was a definite pressure—but one without which the book would never have been finished!

Please enjoy and, I hope, apply the activities clustered in the acronym CELEBRATIONS.

—Allan R. Handysides,
M.B., Ch.B., FRCPC, FRCSC, FACOG

CHAPTER 1

ATTITUDE

Happy the man whose wish and care
A few paternal acres bound,
Content to breathe his nature air
In his own ground.
—*"Solitude," Alexander Pope*

I was walking across the parking lot to the hospital when I saw a police cordon blocking the sidewalk, forcing pedestrians such as myself to walk around to the other hospital entrance. As I took the detour I noticed children from the local church school, where my sister was the elementary school principal, walking around the cordoned-off area on their way to school. Then, to my amazement a young woman in school uniform, but from the high school, walked up to the yellow plastic barrier, grabbed it in her hands, and ripped it apart. She then walked directly through the forbidden area.

As she neared to stride past me, I touched her on the shoulder. "Take your hands off me!" she shouted. "Don't touch me!" The anger in her eyes and the contempt with which she looked at me spoke volumes. She had what is often called an attitude.

We all have "attitude"—whether we are conscious of it or not. The question is, what kind of attitude?

Several words are similar to attitude. I think of *altitude*—one's height in relation to sea level. *Latitude* and *longitude*—one's position in relation to the grid constructed to map the world.

With these three words in mind we can see that *attitude* is the position from which we relate to the world—a mind-set point, if you will. As individuals, our attitude determines life's balance. We see the world revolving, often, around our mind-set. Attitude is the point of view from which we integrate all of our relationships. Attitude is the tone that colors our life—and often the lives of our friends.

Once at the Washington–Dulles airport I watched a huge crane at work. It had a tall central column, and pivoting around a point near its summit it swung loads from one place to another. The hook hung from a transverse beam; a counter-balancing weight hung from the opposite side of the beam. All activity and force centered on this fulcrum point.

As I watched, I thought how crucial the balancing point was to the crane. In a similar way our attitude is a balance point. Our mind-set—or attitude, if you wish—is as crucial to our daily functioning as the pivotal point is to the crane.

Attitude governs the scope of our influence, the radius of our reach. Our ability to carry life's burdens depends upon our lives being in balance. We measure our relationships with others and our assessment of their mind-set by reference to our own. In politics we hear talk of right and left wing—but in reference to what? We hear others judged as conservative or liberal—but such categorization is referenced to the mind-set of the observer.

As a youngster I remember watching a movie called *The Dam Busters*. It told the story of how the Royal Air Force sought to destroy German industrial capability by bombing and thus breaking open Germany's dams. Lacking the sophisticated equipment of today, they worked out a simple solution. They were able to fix two spotlights on the undercarriage of their bombers, and by bringing the two spotlights to convergence they could accurately set their sights above the water of the dam. And by calculating the speed, height, and bounce of a bomb over the water when dropped from this predetermined height, they were able to calculate the point at which the bombs should be released.

Those spotlights demarcated the point from which a calculated action would commence.

SPOTLIGHTS OF ATTITUDE

As I considered spotlights, I had the thought that some spotlights illuminate our attitude. Considering it further, I found four that I believe are of great importance in defining the unique attitude each of us has.

Thought Patterns. This spotlight relates to our way of thinking: the pattern of thought, the content of thought, the quality of our thoughts.

Self-Evaluation. The second is our level of self-appreciation, our concept of self-worth, how much we value our own lives.

Valuation of Others. The third is the value we assign to the lives of others—their hopes, joys, and sorrows.

Belief in a Higher Power. The fourth spotlight illuminating our attitude relates to our belief in a higher power, to our connection with God.

THOUGHT PATTERNS

We are taught how to think. Much of our appreciation of the world around us is learned from those who teach us—our parents, siblings, and other family members. We learn cause and effect—that fire burns and cold stings. We can learn to be cynical or learn to be loving. Our thought patterns reflect the nurturing we received—or our lack of it. It is important to recognize that the way we think often reflects the thinking patterns of our parents and extended family, the schools we attended, and the society around us. Of course, we have innate intellectual abilities and personality traits, but though these influence our emotional thought patterns and possibly the appeal of some concepts, to a large extent we reflect the thinking of our peers. In fact some feel the Jesuits are correct when they say, "Give us a child until he is 7, and he will be forever Catholic." Our early lives definitely shape the person we will become.

When used by mind controlling regimes such as fascist or communist control groups, brainwashing can change a person's thought patterns.

You and I can readily move into extreme positions if we follow unbalanced thought processes. It was Dwight Eisenhower who observed that the extreme positions taken in debate are never correct. When we find ourselves in the extreme, we should carefully analyze our thought processes to see whether we are, in fact, projecting an unbalanced attitude because of learned patterns of thinking.

For Christians there is a solution to unbalanced thinking that may lead to extremism: "Let this mind be in you which was also in Christ Jesus" (Phil. 2:5). This is the Jesus who did not condemn the woman caught in adultery, but pointed out a better way. This is the Jesus who railed against hypocrisy and urged integrity. This is the humble Jesus who urged the abandonment of pride, arrogance, and control of others. This is the mind of Jesus who invited little children to come to Him. This is the Jesus who urged us to adopt the guileless simplicity of a child, to eschew the conniving scheming of the Pharisees. This is the Jesus who was filled with compassion for the suffering, who empathized with the mourning, who cared for sinners. We can choose to be like Jesus.

But to be like Jesus we must train our minds to think as Jesus did. Remember that both fatigue and boredom can cause us to think and do things we normally would not. If we are serious about having a mind like that of Jesus we'll also avoid overeating, in fact, overindulgence in anything, for these can change the brain's neurochemical balance.

And no matter how balanced we usually are, we can fall into the trap of obsessing about something that worries us. We can dissect a situation down to a hundred terrible "what-ifs," making it impossible to truly see the whole. And so we do what Jesus warned us about, we "strain out a gnat and swallow a camel" (Matt. 23:24).

Ancient philosophers learned the power of fasting—the clarity of thought that comes when the mind is freed from the chemical bombardment of food. It's something to consider when you are wrestling with a puzzling problem.

And though this probably is *not* you, millions today alter their brain's chemistry with drugs, including the legal ones such as tobacco and alcohol. We may think it's easy to change our thought patterns, but many recovering addicts find, to their chagrin, that their drug use has altered neuronal pathways. This is particularly true for young adults and children.

SELF-EVALUATION

Our second determinant of attitude is how we value ourselves. This too is learned. Psychologists tell us that by age 3 most children have learned a sense of self-worth. It is extremely important for you to value yourself. If you don't value yourself, you will have no motivation to take care of yourself, your body, soul, or spirit. And if you don't value yourself, it is very difficult for you to accept the infinite value God has placed on your life!

But thinking too much of yourself will make you arrogant and proud, perhaps willful and demanding. Your relationships with others may not be give and take, but only take. People who are unable to give don't always recognize the work others do for them. It becomes second nature to blame all of life's difficulties on the deficiencies of others, never for a moment believing they could ever be responsible. It goes without saying that people like this are difficult to love.

At the other extreme are those who feel so utterly hopeless, so worthless, that they are unable to accept love. Sometimes they construct, from their pain, a shell of protection, and so are perceived as prickly and hard to work with. They may build themselves up by pulling others down, yet they never seem to achieve success—surely nothing that satisfies them. Because realistic self-worth is learned, and because self-absorption is often a distortion of reality, the attitudes of those at either extreme are often distorted and unrealistic.

However, there is a solution.

Jesus looks at our distorted self-images, and offers a simple solution: "Follow Me."

Sitting up in a tree, the little tax collector positioned himself above the crowd. Despised by others and despising himself, Zacchaeus had tried to find happiness through wealth and opulence. Yet, despite all the security his money could buy, he was consumed by the "small man" syndrome—he could never be tall enough, or rich enough, or good enough, and deep in his heart he knew it.

But Jesus knew his need for recognition and appreciation. Jesus knew his desperate quest for value, and Jesus had come to change his life.

Jesus knows *my* need for recognition, *my* desire to be appreciated. And He knows yours.

Stopping below the sycamore tree, Jesus looked up into the leafy branches and said, "Zacchaeus." In that one word, He gave the despised tax collector recognition, acknowledgement, and respect. In speaking his name, Jesus welcomed him as a friend, companion, and associate. Then, inviting Himself to dinner, He thrilled the lonely, miserable little heart of Zacchaeus with the joy of recognition.

Jesus calls you and me by name, urging, "Come to me, all you who are weary and burdened" (Matt. 11:28, NIV). I recognize myself there, don't you? If we can only appreciate that we are valued by Jesus, we will lose the self-doubt and the artificial crutches of arrogance and pride. We will lose the need to correct others, to be seen as knowing so much, and the desire to be important in the eyes of others. Why? Because we are important to Jesus.

VALUATION OF OTHERS

The third spotlight upon our attitude is the value we bestow to others—or lack of it. Of course, often we are unaware of our behavior and the way we come across to others. That happened to me not long ago.

I had organized a meeting and was arranging for different people to do different things. In the middle of pointing out the duties I assigned to each one, I was stopped cold by an associate who was never backward in pointing out the deficiencies of others. She began to imitate my behavior: "*You* do this and *you* do that!"

She stopped me dead in my tracks. Is that what I looked like—a mini-dictator? Right or wrong, she gave me pause for thought.

We all need to pause and think, *How do I value others? What do my words and actions show that I think of others?*

We are at our most natural in our homes, around those closest to us. They're the ones who see us when we are our truest selves. It takes only a few years for the idolized husband to develop a pot belly, lose his hair, and gain some bad habits. Nor does the princess look so glamorous in the morning in a wrinkled T-shirt and sleep creased face devoid of makeup. Yet it is in the home when these realities become unavoidable that our true evaluation of another becomes obvious. When we learn to love despite the blemishes, warts, bumps, and bald patches, we show that we truly value the other person.

The Bible talks of not trusting someone who winks and nods, and we all recognize the rolling of eyes as a sign of devaluing another. Yet the value we give, or don't give, may simply reflect the value we have of ourselves.

We can destroy a reputation by talking critically of a friend or associate, saying things we'd never say to their face. It can make us feel good for a moment, telling a bit of dirt that the other doesn't know. But by so doing we tell a lot about ourselves, for the value we place on others shines a spotlight on our own attitudes.

The snort of disdain, the snicker or sneer—all tell more of our attitude than of the person devalued, and the wise listener will recognize our attempt to build ourselves up by putting someone else down.

Walking along, surrounded by a crowd of people, suddenly Jesus felt healing power go out from Him (see Mark 5: 24-32). He immediately stopped walking and asked who had touched Him, inwardly thrilled that someone had crept up to Him, had placed such faith and such confidence in Him that they stole a cure. He waited. The crowd parted, and a trembling woman came forward. Jesus looked at her—this woman of faith who had bled for 12 years—and she looked at Him. "Your faith has made you well," Jesus said. "Go in peace."

In that encounter, both the sick woman and the Man she touched accorded the other immense value. If we could look upon others as we look upon Jesus, we would become like Him.

It is no wonder that the first commandment is to love the Lord our God with all our hearts. It is this commandment that makes possible the second: to love our neighbor as ourselves (Luke 10:27). You see, in loving others we become more like Jesus. To understand our attitude, we need to carefully examine how we think about and behave toward others—family, friends, or strangers.

BELIEF IN A HIGHER POWER

The fourth spotlight upon attitude shines from the way we think of God.

Atheists have no Lord to tell them, "This is the way, walk in it"—so they must construct a system of ethics that revolves around human philosophy. Humanism has replaced God and yet, because without God there is difficulty in finding meaning in life, a system of values becomes intangible. So we see the rise of hedonism. "If it feels good, do it," and "As long as it doesn't hurt somebody else . . ." become the mantras of many.

But if there is no purpose or meaning to life, how can there be value? If value is merely what I place on something, what if I don't value you? Society without God becomes a disrespectful place. People are viewed as potentially advantageous or disadvantageous to my personal advancement. Yet, to where and from where do I advance? Without meaning in life, who determines that my success is, in fact, success? Without meaning, nothing really matters. Without an all-powerful God, relativism becomes meaningless—and therefore, so do relationships. Somewhere a standard must exist upon which we can calibrate life's value.

When Moses stood before the burning bush in the desert of the Sinai, he questioned the Voice, the authority of the One directing him to go back to Egypt. "Who shall I say sent me?" he asked. The mysterious answer: "Say to the Israelites, 'I AM has sent me to you'" (see Ex. 3)— incomprehensibly profound, beyond calculation by even the mind of Einstein. Only hinted at in the theories of relativity, "I AM" encompasses all time, all existence. This is the God who sustains all, who is the mystery of existence, who is beyond our comprehension—yet who characterized Himself in bare stick outlines that humans could, at least, vaguely understand. This is the God who, by coming incarnate, displayed infinite love through the life of Jesus. Our attitude is illuminated by our appreciation and concept of the Higher Power.

Haughty and proud, we may deny His existence. Doubtful and timid, demanding proof on our own terms, we may be agnostic. Fearful, afraid of our worth, we may deny His interest in us as individuals.

Yet Jesus, standing before Jerusalem, mourned, "Jerusalem, Jerusalem, . . . how often I wanted to gather your children together, as a hen gathers her chicks under her wings, but you were not willing!" (Matt. 23:37)

When we look at these four illuminating perceptions—our thought patterns, our self-worth, how we value others, and our belief about God—we see that our view of God influences the first three. So it is that our attitude reveals much of our worldview, and our worldview reflects our view of God.

Those who see God as loving and kind will have a different perspective from those who view Him as harsh.

The gratefulness of those who trust Jesus as their Savior—people who recognize His life and death as a free gift to a sin-sick world—will affect every area of their lives.

Having walked through what David calls "the valley of the shadow of death," those who recognize Jesus as their Savior will have a different attitude than those whose belief system does not include a loving Father who walks that "valley" with them.

Someone has said that there are passwords to get into heaven. The pearly gates stand wide-open, but those who would pass through must say the words with heartfelt truth. The words reflect one's attitude because attitude is the key to entering heaven.

Do you want to know the passwords? I will tell you. They are easy, they are gentle, but you must be sincere when you speak them.

Here are the passwords, the essence of life's meaning: *Thank You, Jesus!*

An attitude of appreciation does not bind you in a humiliating bondage. Rather, it releases you to freely serve others. It is this freedom that leads to a further attitude—celebration. Celebration goes beyond simple appreciation to applying within our lives that which we appreciate—the life of Jesus. When, through the Holy Spirit, we experience the fullness of freedom, our whole life becomes a celebration.

Paul wrote, "For the law of the Spirit of life in Christ Jesus has made me free from the law of sin and death" (Rom. 8:2). So saying, Paul recognized that the agencies of evil are powerful and pervasive, but he exulted over the saving power of the Spirit, ending that passage with these triumphant words:

"For I am persuaded that neither death nor life, nor angels nor principalities nor powers, nor things present nor things to come, nor height nor depth, nor any other created thing, shall be able to separate us from the love of God which is in Christ Jesus our Lord" (Rom. 8:38, 39).

For many years my father preached with fervor and conviction the message of salvation through the grace of Jesus. With that influence, it was natural for me to accept God's grace as a certainty. My dear wife, Janet, who became an Adventist in her early twenties, often agonized, wondering if she were good enough for heaven. I often told her that she—like every one of us—was *not* good enough for heaven, but Jesus was, and He died so that anyone who wanted entry as His special guest could be admitted. However, Janet did not internalize this until she read Philip Yancey's book

What's So Amazing About Grace? And once she experienced the emancipating power of grace, she became a new woman. Confident in Jesus, she no longer questions her salvation. No longer does she worry and struggle to achieve compulsive obedience. Rather, she lives with celebratory compassion and caring, as would Jesus. No longer is her focus on her own anxieties. Instead, she thinks about the needs of others. Her life is full of joyful service, without any thought of reward, because she has claimed all she will ever need—that is, Jesus.

The following chapters will dissect the meaning of life celebrations.

We are "whole" beings—made up of spiritual, mental, physical, and emotional components. With this in mind, we will look at *whole*someness. This is not to detail what we can or cannot do, but rather to learn how best to enjoy the gift of life, for appreciation opens our hearts to celebration and joy.

Jesus still heals today, as always. I hope you will feel His touch as you read this little book.

CHAPTER 2

CHOICES

To see a world in a grain of sand,
And heaven in a wildflower;
Hold infinity in the palm of your hand,
And eternity in an hour.
— *"Auguries of Innocence," William Blake*

C Is for Choices

While working as an obstetrician, I routinely offered certain diagnostic tests to my patients, especially those appropriate to specific conditions. If a patient was near the age of 40, I always told her about the screening tests available for chromosomal abnormalities in her baby. My offer left the decision to the patient, and was necessary to protect me from the charges that I tried to control or remove a patient's freedom of choice.

This certain patient was a Christian, yet I was not sure how she would choose. When my wife was pregnant at age 37, she had firmly declined any definitive chromosomal screening of the fetus, even though she knew the increased risk, so I thought perhaps this patient would do the same. To my surprise, she informed me she wanted the tests to be done.

About two weeks later I received a phone call, telling me that the baby had an extra chromosome—meaning that it was a Down syndrome baby. I had my receptionist call the patient and ask both her and her husband to come to see me that evening. She told them that I needed to discuss the test results with them, that there were details that could be explained only in a personal interview.

Wondering what this couple would choose, when we sat face-to-face I gently unwrapped the implications of the test. I had seen people behave in different ways when presented with such serious news. I knew how important it was to speak directly to the patient, and how important for both parents to be present. Anxiety lined the faces of this couple, but they sat quietly as I explained the situation. Unlike some others, there was no explosive, emotional outburst. I presented the whole spectrum of possible difficulties, and could tell that they fully comprehended the clinical picture. I told them that I personally would not terminate a pregnancy, but that they had a choice as there were other physicians who did not feel the way I did. My patient said, "Doctor, we will think about this, but we will probably not terminate this pregnancy." A couple of days later, the patient came to see me again. This time, she was full of questions, including a request for information about support groups. She returned faithfully for visit after visit, at which times I would check the progress of her pregnancy and her status. I was deeply impressed by her visible calm and clear approach to the new baby, even though she knew it would not be perfectly normal.

The labor was uncomplicated and smooth. It was the mom's third delivery, and she was patient and in great control. As soon as the baby was born, it cried vigorously. It had an excellent Apgar score, and as I handed it up to the mother, she took it eagerly, drawing it to her in loving affection.

I have delivered literally thousands of babies, but none were more joyously welcomed, more lovingly embraced. This mother had made a clear and beautiful choice, and had accepted all the consequences of the choice without reservation. She had chosen to invest the little baby's life with hope. She bestowed upon her baby a meaning, a purpose, a dignity, and respect.

I have heard many seek to abort such babies without considering the importance and value of their lives. John Ortberg, in his book *When the Game Is Over It All Goes Back in the Box,* tells a beautiful story of Johnny the Bagger.

Johnny also had Down syndrome, and worked as a grocery bagger in the local grocery store. And after attending a motivational rally for staff of the retail company, he became convinced that everyone—himself included—could do something to enrich the lives of their customers. So with his father's help, he decided to produce and distribute a little "Thought for the Day." He printed them on his computer, then carefully cut the little messages into strips. One by one he gave them out with a smile and well wishes to the customers he bagged for.

After a few weeks, the manager noted that lines of people formed behind whichever counter Johnny was in bagging the groceries. When customers were invited to go to less populated rows, they declined, saying they wanted Johnny's thought for the day.

Soon others in the store began to think of things they could do to enhance the customers' experience. The florist staff made little corsages from flowers with broken stems, pinning them on to the coats of some of the el-

derly women shopping in the store. At the meat counter ribbons soon dec-
orated the cuts of meat. Soon customer satisfaction and loyalty had skyrock-
eted. Johnny the Bagger showed a little love, a big smile, and a cheery
greeting. It cost very little, but changed the outlook of an entire enterprise.

Johnny didn't have all the opportunities of life, but he chose to do his
best with what he had.

We often think of choice as a basic human right—but not everyone has
the same array of opportunities from which to choose. I have often stood
among the tiny homes of rural African villages, children with big, wide
eyes and ragged clothes gathered around me. Sometimes the flies that lit
on their faces and bodies were not even flicked off, because they were lan-
guid with undernutrition. What choices did such youngsters have?
Mentally I'd compare them to my own children and to those of my
friends. Their opportunities for education were limited. Their food choices
limited to beans and rice, or perhaps rice and beans! Yet Scripture tells us
that "the true light that gives light to every man" came into the world
(John 1:9, NIV). This light of the Holy Spirit illuminates the grace of
Jesus—the Person we all may choose to be our Savior.

One of my friends became an alcoholic. He struggled in the grip of alcohol, tobacco, caffeine, and even illegal drugs. He described a family history
of some four generations of drug dependent family members. "What choice
did I have?" he asked. But then I pointed out that today he is free of the addictive shackles. How could he have done it if he had not made a choice?
Perhaps he should have asked "What opportunities did I have?" Certainly,
the list had been shortened, the possibilities reduced, yet he still had the
power to make decisions and choose, even if from a very shortened list.

Our first chapter dealt with attitude, the viewpoint that often influences
the choices we make. As we have seen, attitude is influenced by others and
to some extent our choices may be restricted. Yet we owe it to ourselves
to think carefully about the choices we make. Every choice carries a consequence, whether for good or bad.

When we carefully consider an issue, we mentally assess the evidence for
or against a given viewpoint. The weight we give to the evidence may—
but not always—reflect the logic or science behind it, for sometimes we
are not sufficiently educated to make a good decision and sometimes emotions play a role in our conclusions. Whether or not the choice is well-in-
formed, its consequences have little to do with our reasons for choosing as
we did. Rather, the consequences are the outworking of the natural laws
surrounding the issue.

In *Blink*, Malcolm Gladwell's book about the reflex-like intelligence he calls "the thin slice," he writes about our almost intuitive beliefs. These, he says, often influence our choices—sometimes fortunately and sometimes not. While our intuitive selections are often correct, they aren't always. If our choice is something simple such as deciding the color of a dress or a tie, the consequences are minimal, but often decisions based on little except intuition are of great importance.

I remember meeting another tourist, Emile, on a packaged vacation trip to Spain. He was Jewish, and as we became friends he related the story of his life. He told me how, as a youngster of 14, he, his sister, and her baby, were taken by Nazi soldiers and crowded in the cattle cars of a train. For two or three nights and days the train rumbled on without stopping, the passengers packed like sardines in the cars. There were no toilet facilities and the poor people were a sorry mess when they were finally herded out of the train. Blinking in the bright light, young Emile was faced with an immediate decision. "Women and children to the right, men to the left," a guard called out. Emile was 14 years old and he had to choose in a flash. With no evidence, he chose to be a man.

The last Emile saw of his sister was her scarf-covered head, her baby on her shoulder, slowly walking toward a fate that included the gas chambers and death. Sometimes the evidence is inconclusive, but our attitude is vitally important. Emile, by his determination to be a man, saved his own life.

One of life's most important choices, and one for which we do not have conclusive scientific evidence, is that of the nature and existence of God. Our belief in God is probably a matter of choice, though a faith perspective enables us to recognize God's influence in the world and in our lives. And despite no definitive scientific proof, the choice to believe in God—or not to believe—has both immediate and long-term results. Most of life's actions reflect our belief system, and belief in God is of enormous consequence.

The consequences involve a major impact upon our attitude, our worldview, and the way we find meaning or lack thereof in life. Yet, more than our quality of life, there is the distinct possibility that whether or not we believe impacts our daily lives and life into eternity—something we cannot even comprehend.

This question of meaning is the most profound we'll ever face. We have to decide whether we'll live our lives in a way that brings meaning to us and others, or whether our lives will be meaningless. Yet how many of us ignore its relevance!

Sometimes it is helpful to our thinking to see how others processed their life questions. With that in mind, I write my own experience. Studying medicine, my education covered the typical sciences of physics, chemistry, and biology and the human functions of physiology and anatomy. The deeper I got into these areas the more I found myself awed by the intricate mechanisms that are so interdependent, so sensitive to specific enzyme action, temperature, and pH balance. Class after class created in me a profound sense of wonder.

Through my years of study I was taught both the theory of evolution and the biblical story of Creation. Recognizing the lack of proof in either scenario, and the difficulties presented by both, I understand how a person may be ambivalent. For me, however, I find it incredible that such complexity came by chance. Indeed, without God in the equation, the whole becomes meaningless. With God removed from our thinking, life—mine and yours—is reduced to equal insignificance of a crystal of rock salt. Morality becomes an invention of the human mind, which itself is merely an invention of chance. Perhaps, from my perspective, I am fortunate that the theory of evolution cannot answer the questions of how, why, what, or when the first independent life began. On the other hand, my life experience has taught me there is goodness, kindness, love, and—within the frame of human experience—a yearning for the satisfaction of meaning. I have, therefore, chosen to believe in a God who cares.

It is amazing, the consequences that accrue to that choice. I find consequences in every aspect of life.

Because life has meaning, it has value. Because we are alive, we have meaning and meaning brings value. My children, my wife, my family, my community—all people of the world are of value.

The consequences of moving beyond chance to purpose and meaning fill my life view with value.

I remember the sixties, when the "establishment" was assailed on all sides. Hippies, with flowers in their hair and pot in their heads, swayed to gentle music and denied "value statements," oblivious to the fact that they were making their own. And much of society today, while permitting most everyone to establish their own values, ultimately denies all value by denying a universal purpose or presence.

Accepting God as real is, then, a fundamental choice. My choice influences not God, but me. My choice must be a total one, if I am to be impacted by it. Then the reality of God becomes an interpretive factor in all my explanation of life. I begin to realize God can seek to influence the thoughts and thinking patterns of His creatures, through revelations in nature and of inspiration.

Examination of the Bible presents a range of choices. Study reveals remarkable coherence in its presentation of a plan of salvation. We recognize the complex contexts in which the Bible was written, that its span covers both time and culture, and yet we see it maintains great homogeneity. Again, we make a choice as to how we interpret the Bible and apply its lessons to our lives.

Recognition of choice as fundamental to our worldview and our worldview to choice becomes a factor in tolerance of not only the opinion of others, but of themselves. To be happy we need to have, and accord to others, freedom of choice. Perhaps freedom itself is in its essence freedom of choice, at least in the area of thought.

One of my office assistants had come to Canada from the former U.S.S.R. I found it fascinating to listen to her explain the workings of a totalitarian regime. In the name of "power to the people," individuals in power removed to whatever extent they could the power of individual choice. Dissidence is not permitted in a totalitarian regime. How unfortunate it is that many who permit themselves freedom of choice would deny others the same freedom. In actuality, it often boils down to a desire to control not only our situation, but others in the orbit of our experience.

My three granddaughters are delightful, at least to my wife and me. They are quite individual in appearance, personality, and spirit, and one of them is particularly independent. Even as a little girl of 2, she insisted on doing things for herself. She needed to be in control. It is a good and happy thing that she has two sisters to help moderate this tendency, for she shows the determination of a Cleopatra. I have no doubt that she has already learned many lessons in cooperative living, but it is not always easy even for adults to practice such lessons.

Freedom of choice not only affects our religious freedom, but that of our lifestyle. Freedom of choice enables us all to celebrate our individuality, but if our choices impact another's and diminish another's choice we may meet the limit of our freedom. Some ask whether lifestyle choices should impact the freedom of others. The smoker who insists on smoking in the workplace or in a car with other commuters may be imposing his smoke on nonsmokers who don't appreciate the toxic fumes. It is in the pursuit of freedom of choice that nonsmokers propose limitations on the areas in which smoking occurs, and that smokers agree to them.

I have a neighbor who has smoked for about 50 years, though smoking has been shown to be related to cancer of the lung and oral cavity. When the first studies were presented on the association in the 1950s in the

United Kingdom, skepticism was expressed, particularly by the tobacco industry. The data showed the relationship to be beyond question, yet many chose to ignore it because they wanted to smoke.

Interesting, yet so tragic, is the story of the U.S. Public Health Service Committee, established by the U.S. Surgeon General in 1962 at the request of President Kennedy. Fifty percent of the committee's members were smokers, purposely selected both as scientists and smokers to prevent the criticism sure to be leveled by tobacco companies that the panel was biased against tobacco. Photographs at the National Library of Medicine show Surgeon General Luther Terry with the committee in a smoke-filled room, conference tables littered with ashtrays. After studying the data, all on the committee agreed that the evidence against cigarettes was overwhelming, yet not all chose to stop smoking. Several were to suffer the consequences of their habit. Read the following excerpt from *The Cigarette Century* by Allan Brandt, pp. 229, 230:

"In the year following the release of the report, Fieser, the heaviest smoker on the committee, was diagnosed with lung cancer. Following the removal of a lung, he wrote to his former colleagues, 'You may recall that although fully convinced by the committee, I continued heavy smoking throughout the deliberations of our committee and invoked all the usual excuses. . . . My case seems to me more convincing than any statistics.' Suffering as well from emphysema, heart disease, and bronchitis, all linked in the report to smoking, Fieser now relinquished his cigarettes once and for all. He wrote to Cochran, urging him to quit as well. 'I recommend total nonsmoking, for it certainly makes you feel better,' Fieser told his Harvard colleague. 'I have not smoked since August 27 and do not find abstinence particularly painful.' Disease and looming mortality fractured denial with a power that the most intimate acquaintance with the data could not match."

Freedom of choice means freedom to do the wrong thing. Strange as it may seem, the celebration of choice has to include permission for poor choices. We may find it hard to celebrate the ability to make a poor choice until we consider the other side of the coin, which permits good choices. It is here that the foundational choice of belief in God is so important, for God—as presented in the Bible—has offered to *all* the choice of Jesus as one's personal Savior. "For God so loved the world that He gave His only begotten Son, that whoever believes in Him should not perish but have eternal life" (John 3:16).

Perhaps the clearest association between choice and consequence lies in the area of health. It is well known that many of our health practices directly bear on how long we can expect to live. How important we judge a given lifestyle practice, and how much we choose to accommodate such a practice in our personal lifestyle is a personal choice of significant consequence.

My wife and I have chosen to be vegetarians because we consider it a healthful lifestyle, and our three children have adopted this lifestyle with varied degrees of acceptance. It is for them that such a choice offers the greatest lifelong potential, yet it is strange—youth often does not regard health as precious as do those of us who are older.

Drs. Nedra Belloc and Lester Breslow, from the Department of Public Health, Berkeley, California, were among the first researchers to present convincing evidence on lifestyle habits that promote longevity. In their classic study of 6,928 adult residents of Alameda County, California, they discovered seven habits that positively influence how long a person lives. They are:

1. Adequate sleep (7 to 8 hours per night)

2. No eating between meals

3. A nutritious daily breakfast

4. Maintenance of the recommended weight for one's height, bone structure, and age

5. Regular physical activity

6. Reduction of alcoholic beverages (We suggest nonuse as the better choice.)

7. Nonuse of tobacco

A nine-year follow-up revealed that the number of healthful lifestyle habits a person followed related directly to their likelihood of dying or not. During this period, only 5.5 percent of men and 5.3 percent of women who followed *all seven habits* died, compared to a mortality of 20 percent in men and 12.3 percent in women who followed three or fewer of these habits in the same time period.

- To exercise or not is a choice.

- To drink sufficient water or not is a choice.

- To be pessimistic or optimistic is a choice.

- To be sexually chaste or not is a choice.

- To trust God or not is a choice.

My wife and I were in a restaurant with my father-in-law. Janet and I ordered a vegetarian dish and to our surprise, he did too. We knew he loved his steak and lamb chops, so were interested to learn why. "I have listened to you talking about the benefits of eating less meat, and I think I am going to be vegetarian myself," he told us. I almost laughed out loud, but in deference congratulated him instead. The reason I found it laughable was that he was 83 years old with severe health issues. I didn't think becoming vegetarian at this stage of life would have much influence on his longevity. Then I thought of a choice he could make that would be far more predictive of his welfare—to invite Jesus to be his personal Savior.

How many reading this chapter will make that choice? You can make it at any age, whether you are well or sick, in the prime of life or nearing its end—and it carries eternal consequences.

CHAPTER 3

FAITH IS EXERCISE

For while the tired waves, vainly breaking,
Seem here no painful inch to gain,
Far back, through creeks and inlets making,
Comes silent, flooding in the main.
—*"Say Not the Strange Naught Availeth," Arthur Hugh Clough*

E Is for Exercise: The Elixir of Our Energy

Tucked into the New Testament like a sweet jalapeño pepper in a veggie sandwich is the little book of James. More emphatically than the stories we read in the Gospels, the wonder of Acts, or the theology of Romans, James exhorts us to our responsibility of action.

"Faith?" he asks. "Show me your faith, and I'll show you mine by my deeds."

Hebrews 11 lists the heroes of faith, and James, mentioning only a few, shows they acted upon their faith. In separating the sheep from the goats, Jesus points not to a difference in belief but in action. "Inasmuch as you did it to one of the least . . ." (Matt. 25:40). Christianity in its purest form is not a list of doctrines; it does not reach its zenith in lyrical, poignant, or articulate argument and prose. Rather pure Christianity is seen visiting the widows and fatherless and those afflicted. In Philippians 4:8, Paul admonishes us to think on things pure and graceful, lovely and of a good report—but in the next verse he emphatically commands the readers to do.

Ellen White wrote, "The only way to grow in grace is to be disinterestedly *doing* the very work which Christ has enjoined upon us—to engage, to the extent of our ability, in helping and blessing those who need the help we can give them. Strength comes by exercise; activity is the very condition of life. Those who endeavor to maintain Christian life by passively accepting the blessings that come through the means of grace, doing nothing for Christ, are simply trying to live by eating without working. And in the spiritual as in the natural world, this always results in degeneration and decay. A man who would refuse to exercise his limbs would soon lose all power to use them. Thus the Christian who will not exercise his God-given powers not only fails to grow up into Christ, but he loses the strength that he already had" (*Steps to Christ*, pp. 80, 81, emphasis supplied).

I remember well a certain intern I was training. It was her first day on our service and she was assigned to assist in surgery. Having always had an inclination to teach, I started at the scrub sinks. The antiseptic preps were the topic of discussion; dangers of chemical burns if too much were slopped out and ran to the patient's back, the importance of physical debridement or scrub, the advantage of clipping hair rather than shaving the skin.

After teaching the "prep" in detail, as indeed for a hysterectomy it must be performed, the drapes were carefully placed and the towel clips attached. I wanted to disabuse the intern of the miserable practice of some of my colleagues who actually pinned the drapes to the patient's skin with clips—whose puncture points most certainly caused postoperative pain. We discussed the types of incisions and their pros and cons.

Then the incision itself—how important to hold the knife correctly so as to avoid a beveled incision. I demonstrated how important it is to cut at right angles to the surface. Then there was homeostasis, the use of the cautery, and the use of mosquito snaps. Anatomical layers were described and incised.

For me, it was important for the intern to understand that respect for a person includes the delicate handling of their tissues. No "cowboy" slash and burn, no "slitting" or "slicing," "grabbing" or "tearing," but "incising" and "teasing," "retracting" and "dissecting." By listening to the surgeon's language you can tell a lot about their training, or lack thereof.

Moving with the ease of my having done a couple hundred of the procedure, it was soon a matter of retreating from the field, repairing each layer with meticulous care, repeating the mantra of my old mentor, Walter Hannah, "What God hath put together let no surgeon leave asunder." Apposing the skin edges with care, no little flaps lying raw to scab and possibly get infected, I finished the surgery a proud surgeon.

I looked at the intern. "Well, that was easy," she said. "I think I could do it." I recognized the intended praise, but also heard a lack of comprehension of the details she'd just watched. Besides, she had found the service only an hour and a half ago!

The next case was an encore, another abdominal hysterectomy. (This was before laparoscopically assisted vaginal hysterectomy.) Because she'd just observed one and had expressed her confidence, I handed the intern the scalpel. "You do it. I'll assist."

She looked at the abdomen—draped, prepped, and ready for the incision—then at me. "Where do I make the incision?" she asked. What had looked so easy when someone else did it now took on different perspectives. "Where do I begin?"

Religion is so easy in theory, so attractive to discuss, even stimulating to argue about— but so difficult to practice.

In the booklet, *The Practice of the Presence of God—Conversations and Letters of Brother Lawrence* (Epworth Press, Frank H. Cumbers, 25-35 City Road, ECI London) is described "the exercise of the presence of God," whereby "we are with Him who is our end." Brother Lawrence found that whether sweeping the floor, washing dishes, making beds, or doing ironing, he could live in the conscious awareness of the presence of God and, by so doing, transformed his living into praise. The move from theory into practice, from theology to good works, brought such joy to his life that he was able to be living praise. We, too, should begin living praise by focusing on God's presence everywhere, always, and His personal interest in us as His children.

Living in the presence of God transforms faith from a passive belief to an active living praise. No longer an armchair fan of some activity, we now become participants.

I'm not suggesting that there is no benefit to theory, but it is in the test of practice that our true strengths are revealed. Roger Bannister, in his breaking of the four-minute mile, put into practice the principles of physiology and exercise. By enlisting the support of his two friends, Chris Chataway and Chris Brasher, Bannister recognized the importance of the mental aspect of running. He realized that not only must his muscles be primed, but his mind must be focused, challenged, and stimulated.

In the realm of faith, the apostle Paul compares the race of life to the perseverance of an athlete in chasing a goal. After dedicating Hebrews chapter 11 to the heroes of faith, chapter 12 encourages us to become athletes in the Gospel race. Paul points to the cloud of witnesses, the world in the stands, as it were, and encourages us to run the long-distance race. In this life of living praise we should lay aside every weight, Paul says, referring to the practice of runners in his day who trained by carrying weights on their person. "Lay aside every weight, and the sin which so easily ensnares us" (Heb. 12:1).

Our goal must be clear and fixed. Our focus unwavering. Before participating in the 2008 Olympics, Michael Phelps set a goal of winning more gold medals than any other athlete in history. Training with this goal in sight, he succeeded, and had the world at his doorstep!

Paul urges Christians to keep their eyes on Jesus, "the author and finisher of our faith." O, that everyone would do so. In January 2009, Phelps was photographed smoking marijuana and the photos went round the world. That lapse cost him millions of dollars in endorsements. Paul understood the importance of the spiritual focus, its primacy in success. Unfortunately, taking our eyes from Jesus we often neglect our spiritual health, only to find that we are ensnared by sin which, indeed, does so easily beset us.

Forty-six days after Roger Bannister broke the world record of the four-minute mile, running the distance in three minutes, 59.4 seconds, John Landy of Australia broke Bannister's record in a race in Finland. I well remember the excitement, the buzz over who was the fastest runner. On August 7, 1954, the two runners faced off over the one-mile in the British Empire and Commonwealth Games held in Vancouver, British Columbia.

Advertised at the time as the "miracle mile" and running like the world champion he was, in the third of the four laps John Landy was about 10 yards ahead. Now came the decisive final lap. Both runners began their sprint toward the finish line. Straining every sinew, pumping with all the power possible, these athletes leaned forward to the prize. Then hearing the footsteps pounding closer, perhaps hearing Bannister's gasps for air, Landy looked over his shoulder to see his opponent. Like Lot's wife, the backward glance had great consequences. Bannister surged past, snatching victory from his opponent.

How important that, in the living of praise, the exercise of faith, we keep our eyes fixed on Jesus. In what we can call his valedictory paragraphs, Paul was able to state "I have fought the good fight, I have finished the race, I have kept the faith" (2 Tim. 4:7).

KEEPING FAITH MEANS LIVING PRAISE

There is more to keeping faith than entertaining or even impressing the "cloud of witnesses." Our duty to others is extremely important, but their importance is the same as our importance. We are to love them as we love ourselves, but living praise, keeping faith means we enjoy the grace of Jesus in our lives. Practicing the presence of God transforms our faith into the very experience of heaven, here and now. The weak are able to be strong

and the slow become swift, for the battle is not by power or might, but by His Spirit. This understanding allowed Solomon to write:
"The race is not to the swift,

Nor the battle to the strong,

Nor bread to the wise,

Nor riches to men of understanding" (Eccl. 9:11).

Living praise means *knowing Him* whom we praise.

A young man often seeks to impress a young woman with flattery. Such words may fascinate and captivate, but only if they contain enough truth to be believable. One has to know the object of affection sufficiently to be able to praise in a meaningful way.

In some cultures carrying significant extra weight is considered attractive while other cultures appreciate the slim and slender lines of the well fit. In an attempt to please, I have heard people of the first culture make the faux pas of complimenting an American woman on her plumpness. Without knowing the object of praise, it is difficult to praise! Hence, the first and imperative foundation in "living praise" is to know Him whom we would praise.

Knowing God as the Creator, the Redeemer, the Comforter, the Father, the Brother, requires that we bring Him our whole being. As lovers bring their minds, their spirit, their social activities, even their bodies together, so with God we praise with our whole being.

Many of us believe that healthful living is predicated by what we do *not* do. We do *not* smoke, we do *not* drink alcohol, we do *not* eat meat, and perhaps do *not* drink milk. But health is much more than this—it is how we live!

EXERCISE. GET A LIFE.

In the past few years the phrase "Get a life" has come into parlance. Perhaps directed at couch potatoes, at some abject nerd slaving over a computer, or a one-track student focused only on passing an exam, the phrase decries a one-sided, unbalanced life. That phrase comes to my mind as I think of the privilege of praising God with our bodies. We truly need to "get a life," to be able to praise God with all areas of our lives. And yet one area is neglected by most of us. That area is exercise.

I so enjoy the story of Elijah, a prophet of human proportions—so majestic when moved by the Spirit, so obviously weak within, so obviously empowered from without. After the glory of Mount Carmel and the triumph of the true God, with "the hand of the Lord upon him" Elijah ran ahead of Ahab to the entrance of Jezreel. Though surely God gave him strength for such an achievement, he must have been fit too. Obviously he praised the Lord in the agility of his body. Then I think of King David who danced before the Lord. David used his whole body to express his joy for what God was doing for him and Israel.

Some of us would like to dance before God, but many of us can only creak.

I know two people, Elie Honoré and his wife Marie Elise, who have learned to give living praise as they exercise. They use the CELEBRATIONS acronym to provide a framework of meditation while they walk. When they began systematic walking Marie had pains in her joints and Elie felt breathless with even light exercise. But rather than focusing on their painful bodies, they thought of God and decided to praise Him as they walked. They began by walking short distances, little by little increasing both their pace and the distance. Often they sang together as they strode along. Soon they were covering four miles each morning, and meditating for the whole hour on the love of God. They had found the way to live their praise.

So many are unhealthy and not at all fit. When it comes to exercise, FIT is another useful acronym. The F stands for *frequency*, the I for *intensity*, and the T for the *time* or duration. If we would be living praise, we need to be fit.

Writing in *Ministry of Healing*, pages 237, 238, Ellen White penned these words:

"Action is a law of our being. Every organ of the body has its appointed work, upon the performance of which its development and strength depend. The normal action of all the organs gives strength and vigor, while the tendency of disuse is toward decay and death. Bind up an arm, even for a few weeks, then free it from its bands, and you will see that it is weaker than the one you have been using moderately during the same time. Inactivity produces the same effect upon the whole muscular system."

Such exercise has to engage our whole being—our minds, our spirit, and our body. Some feel too old to exercise, yet science has shown that despite your age, exercise benefits those who do it. In 1998 the *Oregonian* published a story about 103-year-old Ben Levinson. He had set a new world record for shot-put for men more than 100 years old, throwing the ball 10 feet and 1.25 inches.

"Ha!" you say. "The record for centenarians!" But that is his achievement. At 90 he was depressed and frail, shuffling around, ready for the grave. Lack of exercise had led to muscle wasting and dependency.

Urged on by personal trainer David Crawley, Ben began an exercise program. "Feel 80 again, Ben!" Crawley encouraged. Ben "grew" two inches, and with his 20 minutes of daily walking at 2.5 miles per hour and weight training three or four times a week, he soon was a different person. *Regular exercise can do the same thing for you.*

BENEFITS OF PHYSICAL EXERCISE

Regular exercise is not only a preventive measure, it also works to maintain health at its best. The many benefits of physical exercise[1, 2] include the following:

- Exercise makes you more energetic and gives a sense of well-being.

- Exercise helps lower high blood pressure. The *New England Journal of Medicine* published a study that found that aerobic exercise significantly lowered blood pressure in hypertensive patients.[3] Medication is usually essential for the management of hypertension, but in consultation with your personal physician, a regular exercise program can help control your blood pressure.

- Exercise strengthens your bones. Research conducted at Washington University School of Medicine in St. Louis demonstrated that a woman can increase her bone mass by two to three percent per year by doing weight-bearing exercise (over the duration of the study).[4]

- Exercise promotes an increase in HDL cholesterol (good cholesterol). A study of nearly 3,000 men revealed that exercise was associated with higher HDL levels in a dose-response relationship[5]

- Exercise may help manage your diabetes. Harvard researchers documented that exercise *decreases* the risk of developing diabetes in adulthood.[6] Exercise increases the ability of muscle membranes to transport glucose into muscle cells. This particular transportation is not dependent on insulin, and so results in a lowering of the insulin requirement. Sustained, regular exercise leads to a prolonged improvement in insulin sensitivity.[7]

- Exercise may decrease your risk of certain cancers. Epidemiological studies suggest a decrease in colon cancer in people who engage in regular exercise.[8]

- Much of the benefit of exercise comes with the new mitochondria that are formed in the new muscle cells. As the new muscle fibers develop from stem cells within the muscles being exercised, they develop rejuvenated, more efficient mitochondria that carry the youthful properties of new cells. Exercise is, in reality, rejuvenating!

- Exercise improves your quality of life. A consensus panel convened by the National Institutes of Health identified other important benefits in quality of life from exercise such as better mental health, less stress, less anxiety, and less depression.[9]

- Exercise improves communication in those with Alzheimer's disease. In a study examining communication skills of two groups of Alzheimer's patients, more than 40 percent of the group in a walking exercise program experienced significant improvement in communication skills. The group who were given conversation lessons instead experienced no significant improvement.[10]

- Exercise can improves your mental health. A study of patients not suffering from Alzheimer's disease showed measurable improvement in memory after participating in an aerobic exercise program of nine to 10 weeks duration.[11] With increased activity older Americans showed improvement in mental function. There is a clear linear relationship between the level of activity and the level of mental ability.[12] "Through regular, active use of the body, one can discover a greater sense of well-being, far greater vitality, and a calmer, more relaxed attitude toward daily pressures."[13]

- Exercise improves cardiac function. It strengthens the heart, making it more efficient, pumping a greater volume of blood in each contraction.

RECOMMENDED EXERCISE

There are three general types of exercise:

- aerobic, or endurance exercise

- flexibility, or stretching exercise

- strength-building exercise, such as resistance training and weight lifting

Although all are important, aerobic exercise is highly recommended because of its positive effect on the total cardiovascular and pulmonary systems and the body as a whole. The greatest benefit is for those who expend more than 3,500 calories per week in exercise. However, great benefit is obtained even from exercising and expending as little as 750 calories per week.[14]

It is important to note that incidental physical activity is not synonymous with exercise. "Exercise is physical activity that is planned, structured, repetitive, and purposive in the sense that improvements or maintenance of physical fitness is an objective." [15]

What is fitness? According to the American College of Sports Medicine, "Fitness is the ability to perform moderate to vigorous levels of physical activity without undue fatigue."[16] General examples of **moderate exercise** (expending 150 calories) reported by the U.S. Surgeon General are as follows:

- running for 15 minutes

- playing basketball for 15-20 minutes

- swimming laps for 20 minutes

- raking leaves or active gardening for 30 minutes

- brisk walking for 30 minutes

- playing volleyball for 45 minutes

Dr. Kenneth Cooper, of aerobics fame, promotes low intensity exercise, such as brisk walking, in contrast to running, because 48 percent of those who jog/run from 1 to 20 miles per week suffer injuries to their joints and/or muscles. Walking appeals to most of us because it can be done at almost any time or place. It is fun, convenient, inexpensive, and a form of exercise that we can enjoy alone or with friends. It requires no special equipment. Comfortable walking shoes and clothing are all we need. Brisk walking results in minimal injuries, while exercising most muscles and systems of our bodies. It stimulates the release of endorphins with resultant mood elevation.

"Walking, in all cases where it is possible, is the best exercise, because in walking, all the muscles are brought into action."[17]

In 1995 the Centers for Disease Control and the American College of Sports Medicine published their recommendation that every "adult should accumulate 30 minutes or more of moderate-intensity physical activity on most, preferably all, days of the week."[18]

EXERCISE "TRAINING" HEART RATE

When assessing peak exercise performance, the maximum heart rate would be approximately 220 beats per minute minus one's age. This figure, called the maximum heart rate (MHR), is used as a measure to help calculate a training heart rate (THR) which is 60 to 80 percent of this maximal rate.

For a 50-year-old, the maximum heart rate is 170. This is calculated by subtracting the age, i.e., 50, from 220. When exercising, a target heart rate for a 50-year-old would normally aim for between 102 beats to 136 beats per minute (60 to 80 percent of the MHR). To condition the heart for its optimal performance, the training heart rate needs to be sustained for 20 to 30 minutes.

TRAINING HEART RATE
(60-80 percent of the MHR)

AGE RANGE	HEART/PULSE RATE PER MINUTE
20 – 24	120 – 160
25 – 29	117 – 156
30 – 34	114 – 152
35 – 39	111 – 148
40 – 44	108 – 144
45 – 49	105 – 140
50 – 54	102 – 136
55 – 59	99 – 132
60 – 64	96 – 128
65 – 69	93 – 124
70 – 74	90 – 120

This table can be used to show the desired age-related pulse rate for a person achieving adequate aerobic exercise. This level of exercise improves cardiovascular efficiency and oxygen transportation to the tissues of the body. An easy method of checking the pulse rate is to count the pulse over a six-second interval and multiply by 10.

Though moderate exercise is beneficial, excessive exercise, to the point of exhaustion, can be counterproductive.[19]

- A feeling of well-being follows adequate exercise.

- A person who is exercising and experiences persistent fatigue may be exercising excessively.

Common pitfalls related to exercise include:

- failure to stretch and warm up

- inadequate hydration

- excessive exercise

- inadequate cooling off

- overtraining

- undertraining

- use of improper shoes or equipment

- exercising on nonresilient, irregular, or uneven surfaces

- exercising in excessive heat

- injudicious exercise after being habitually inactive

- ignoring known congenital or diagnosed conditions

- ignoring your body's symptoms

We have already mentioned the useful acronym for remembering the elements in an exercise program is FIT:

F = frequency

I = intensity

T = time

Frequency: Should be at least two to three times per week, preferably daily.

Intensity: The following information applies to healthy people. (A person on medication should consult with their physician prior to engaging in an exercise program.) Intensity should be proportionate to the fitness level. Consult the training heart rate chart previously referred to. If your heart rate during exercise is above the highest number for your age group, slow down. If it is below the lower number, increase the intensity in consultation with your physician.

Time: The duration of exercise should range from a minimum of 20 minutes at your training heart rate up to a complete one-hour training program, which will include stretching and warm-up exercise, some 20 minutes of aerobics, some 20 minutes of strengthening exercise, and some 10 minutes of stretching and flexibility exercises.

PROPER TRAINING CLOTHING

You should wear lightweight garments that offer maximum freedom of movement and are appropriate to your climate. Some modern fabrics keep moisture out while permitting perspiration to escape. Avoid rubberized material, which traps heat and moisture. When exercising in an urban area, wear brightly colored garments for safety. Reflector materials may improve your visibility to others.

Women should pay particular attention to supportive garments such as fitness bras.

PROPER TRAINING SHOES

Your feet bear the weight of your whole body, so it is important that your shoes be comfortable, well-fitting, and supportive. Remember to wear athletic shoes that have about one-half to one inch between the tip of toes and the front of the shoe, plenty of absorbent cushion, good arch support, a solid and snug heel cup, good flexibility, good breathability, and good lacing to adjust tightness without pinching. Shop for shoes in the evening when your feet are somewhat swollen in order to achieve a better fit.

In living praise, we present ourselves the "living sacrifice" the Bible calls for. In praising with our whole being—spiritual, mental, and physical—we truly learn to seek the Lord.

When Moses addressed the children of Israel just before their entry into the Promised Land, he recounted the many ways the Lord had led them throughout the previous decades. He reminded them of the miraculous support God had given them and the dreadful consequences of their wrong choices. In detail, Moses outlined the advice he had given them, their lack of faith and trust, and their rebellious spirit. Then telling them that he himself could not enter the Promised Land, Moses pleaded with them that, though surrounded by the pagan nations, they should always seek the Lord.

"You will find Him if you seek Him with all your heart and with all your soul" (Deut. 4:29).

Living praise, exercising faith, and exercising our mind and body are vital parts of seeking God with all our soul.

---

[1] "Physical Activity and Cardiovascular Health. NIH Consensus Development Panel on Physical Activity and Cardiovascular Health," *Journal of the American Medical Association,* July 17, 1996; 276(3): pp. 241-246.

[2] "Surgeon General's report on physical activity and health. From the Centers for Disease Control and Prevention," *JAMA,* Aug. 21, 1996; 276(7): p. 522.

[3] P. F. Kokkinos, P. Narayan, et al., "Effects of regular exercise on blood pressure and left ventricular hypertrophy in African-American men with severe hypertension," *New England Journal of Medicine,* Nov. 30, 1995; 333(22): pp. 1462-1467.

[4] W. M. Kohrt, D. B. Snead, et al., "Additive effects of weight-bearing exercise and

estrogen on bone mineral density in older women," *Journal of Bone and Mineral Research,* Sep. 1995; 10(9): pp. 1303-1311.

[5] P. F. Kokkinos, J. C. Holland, et al., "Miles run per week and high-density lipoprotein cholesterol levels in healthy, middle-aged men: a dose response relationship," *Archives of Internal Medicine,* Feb. 27, 1995 ; 155(2): pp. 415-420.

[6] J. E. Manson, D. M. Nathan, et al., "A prospective study of exercise and incidences of diabetes among U.S. male physicians," *JAMA,* July 1, 1992; 268(1): pp. 63-67.

[7] W. F. Ganong, *Review of Medical Physiology* (Lange Medical Books/McGraw-Hill, 2001), p. 340.

[8] D. C. Nieman, *Fitness and Sports Medicine* (Palo Alto, Calif.: Bull Publishing, 1995), pp. 493-498.

[9] *The Physician & Sports Medicine: The Health Benefits of Exercise* (Part I, 1987) 15: pp. 113-115.

[10] R. Friedman, R. M. Tappen, "The effect of planned walking on communication in Alzheimer's disease," *Journal of the American Geriatric Society,* July 1991; 39(7): pp. 650-654.

[11] R. W. Bowers, et al., "Memory-dependent Reaction Time and Improved Cardiovascular Fitness in Middle-aged Adults," *Medicine & Science in Sports and Exercise,* 1983; 15: p. 117.

[12] L. Clarkson-Smith, A. A. Hartley, "Relationships between physical exercise and cognitive abilities in older adults," *Psychology and Aging,* June 1989; 4(2): pp. 183-189.

[13] D. C. Nieman, *ibid.,* p. 473.

[14] R. S. Paffenbarger, Jr., R. T. Hyde, et al., "The association of changes in physical-activity level and other lifestyle characteristics with mortality among men," *NEJM,* Feb. 25, 1993; 328(8): pp. 538-545.

[15] D. C. Nieman, *ibid.,* p. 31.

[16] *Ibid.*

[17] Ellen G. White, *The Health Reformer,* July 1, 1872.

[18] R. R. Pate, M. Pragg, et al., "Physical activity and public health," *JAMA,* Feb. 1, 1995; 273(5): pp. 402-407.

[19] D. C. Nieman, "Exercise immunology: practical applications," *International Journal of Sports Medicine,* Mar. 1997; 18 Suppl. 1: pp. S91-100.

CHAPTER 4

LIVING WATER

And every tongue through utter drought
Was withered at the root;
We could not speak, no more than if
We had been choked with soot.
— *"The Rime of the Ancient Mariner," Samuel Taylor Coleridge*

L Is For Liquids—the Lubricant That Keeps Us Functioning

I had run about four miles with my friend, Armando Lopes. Rising early,
I'd tapped on his bedroom window just as light had begun to illuminate
the hills and the narrow winding path on which we would run. He whis-
pered "I'm coming," and soon we were off.

Four miles later we sat on our lookout rock, prayed together, then
walked into the village.

This was Lesotho, the mountain kingdom, and the village had about 17
small homes. Seeing a woman sitting on her doorstep, we stopped to chat.
"What single most important need does this village have?" we asked.

She didn't hesitate. "We need a tap in the village."

She told us how every bucket of water had to be fetched from a spring
some 750 meters up the hill, then carried down to the village. The round
trip was one and a half kilometers. This painted a new picture for us of the
value of a bucket of water. We measured the distance, purchased black
PVC piping, and set about protecting the spring. It is important to avoid
putting any back pressure on a spring, lest the water find another point of
egress. Equally, to ensure that the water is not fouled, it has to be protected
from pigs, cows, goats, and poultry. Once the spring was protected, the
water was run halfway down the hill to a tank we built of blocks and plas-
tered with waterproof cement. This broke the pressure on the pipe, and
any overflow was directed through little irrigation trenches to help the
vegetable gardens grow. We had the hospital plumber fix a tap in the village and hook up the water pipe from the tank. Then we called the vil-

lagers together for the official opening of the tap. To the sound of ululating women, the water gushed forcefully from the tap.

Water—clean, pure water—is a life-giving, life-sustaining, health-promoting necessity. No wonder Bible writers and Jesus Himself used water as a metaphor for the sustaining power of God. As Spirit-filled Christians, we become sources of blessing to others, or as the Bible says, fountains of living water.

THE WATER OF LIFE

Two mountains flank the valley where half a mile south of Sychar, Jacob dug the well that bears his name. Many years later Joshua used the mountains of Gerizim and Ebal when he separated the children of Israel. Half the people were placed on Mount Ebal, some 3,077 feet above sea level. The other half were placed on the 2,849-foot Mount Gerizim.

The blessing on those who kept the law was pronounced from Mount Gerizim. The curses that were to attend the lawless were pronounced from Mount Ebal. Yet, regardless of the pronouncements, the water flowing from these mountains seeped into the valley, and was tapped by this well of Jacob.

Dug through limestone to a depth of 105 feet, the well tapped the groundwater of the valley. Over the centuries, the well gave its cool water to many thousands, but none so well-known as Jesus.

Fatigued as He was traveling through Samaria, Jesus rested at Jacob's well while His disciples walked on into Sychar for food. No pump or gravity-fed pipe lessened the labor of the water-carrying women of that day. Sitting without rope or bucket, Jesus watched a village woman approaching. A Samaritan. Samaritans had built a temple on Mount Gerizim, the Mount of Blessing, and they prided themselves on their lineage from Jacob and in the worship of the true God. Fractured from the Jews, worshipping here at Mount Gerizim, they took pride in their ceremonies. This woman, Jesus knew, had a reputation for being promiscuous. She was shunned by many of the town women, for she represented a threat. Her fluttering eyelids and provocative body language spoke to the men who were judged by a different standard. The wives clucked and sniffed in disdain for her ways, yet were secretly fearful of her—so she came alone to the well.

Ropes had worn grooves in the flat stones that formed the well's rim. Two thousand years later archeologists would uncover those stones several feet below the present level of the valley, and they would bear silent testimony to the biblical story.

It was the sixth hour, sometime between 9:00 a.m. and 12:00 noon, and Jesus was weary. He was thirsty as well as tired. But as He watched this woman approach, a new thirst arose in His heart. He pitied her, this outcast, and sensed in her show of braggadocio her inner discomfort and sadness.

Sensitively taking the role of the supplicant, He made a request: "Give Me a drink" (John 4:7). Not one to be bound by custom, nor cowed by any man, the woman spoke the question of her mind: "How is it that You, being a Jew, ask a drink from me, a Samaritan woman?"

She must have been thinking *This man is very forward. What does he want from me?* But as she takes in, with rapid intelligence, His bearing, deportment, and tone of voice, she knows He is safe, straight, and honorable. Jesus recognized her confusion, yet added something even more puzzling. "If you knew the gift of God, and who it is who says to you, 'Give Me a drink,' you would have asked Him, and He would have given you living water."

How strange. How unnerving. A Jew who did not act like one! Telling her of living water, water that flowed forever. What point was this man trying to make? Unsure as to how to respond, she falls back into the refuge of the mundane. "You don't have anything to plumb the well and it's deep. How will you get your water?" Then feeling pride in her heritage, proud that the Samaritans (and not the Jews) owned this well, and proud that she drew water from the same source as the patriarch, she perked up and asked, "Are You greater than our father Jacob, who gave us the well?"

"Whoever drinks of this water will thirst again," Jesus countered, "but whoever drinks of the water that I shall give him will never thirst. But the water that I shall give him will become in him a fountain of water springing up into everlasting life."

We never find out if Jesus received water from the woman's pitcher that day. The discussion ranged from where and how to worship to her many marriages and her current domestic partner. The climax comes when explicitly, unequivocally, Jesus tells her that He is the Messiah, the source of life itself, not a drudgery of existence, but a pure, exuberant life—a fountain streaming with blessing.

The water of life, given by Jesus, becomes a cleansing stream, a revitalizing power, freeing its recipients from guilt, jealousy, and anger. This water brings relief from anxiety, freedom from stress and insecurity. Taking liberally of the grace of Jesus, soaking up His forgiveness, compassion, and love, men and women are set free. Paul says, "It is for freedom that Christ has set us free" (Gal. 5:1, NIV).

At another time Jesus was surrounded by a crowd of thousands and He purposed to feed them. The Passover was soon to come and He wanted them to recognize that He was the Messiah. He may not have been concerned that they learn the lesson immediately, but He knew countless others would learn in the passage of time. So seating everyone on the grassy slope, He held the five small loaves and two fishes and prayed over them. He wanted to show that the simplest of things can be used by God. The people needed to understand that His incarnate body does not limit the power of God. Five simple barley loaves, two small fish—but in God's hands they multiply to feed a multitude until each person has eaten their fill.

All you can eat! Jesus can provide all you can eat and more. Afterward, the disciples gathered up the leftovers—filling 12 baskets! Later, Jesus explained that He is the Bread of Life. The uncomprehending, concrete-thinking multitude think of cannibalism.

But their arguments do not comprehend the spiritual dimension of the meal. During the Feast of Tabernacles, celebrating the annual harvest, Jesus used the abundance of food to invite the multitude to come to Him and be satisfied. "If anyone **thirsts**, let him come to Me and **drink**. He who believes in Me, as the Scripture has said, out of his heart will flow rivers of living water" (John 7:37, 38).

It is strange that, even today, men and women do not recognize the life-giving streams that pour from the life of Jesus. Not recognizing His divinity, they fail to comprehend His power.

A GUSHING RIVER OF LIFE

The ship had sailed for many weeks and supplies of water had dwindled to nothing. Floating off the coast of South America, parched and dry, the sailors finally saw another ship. All hands clambered aboard, shouting and yelling for the ship to stop and give them water. Men on the passing ship shouted for them to dip into the ocean and taste the water. Finally getting the message, someone lowered a bucket into the sea. He took a sip, and a shout went up. The water was fresh! The mighty Amazon, discharging its flood into the ocean, filled this area with fresh, unsalted water.

How many of us, attending church, singing our hymns, have not fully appreciated that the quenching of our thirst is all around us in the love and grace of Jesus. "Taste!" the Bible tells us. "Oh, taste and see that the Lord is good" (Ps. 34:8).

The water of life is not given merely as a cupful. The Spirit fills the Christian life as a fountain, a gushing river of life, of grace, of love, of compassion, and of peace. Psalm 42:1, 2, pictures a frantic deer chased by baying hounds, panting for the water of a cooling stream. David praises God in the words: "O God, You are my God; early will I seek You; my soul *thirsts* for You; my flesh longs for You in a dry and thirsty land where there is no water" (Ps. 63:1).

In Psalm 46 we read "God is our refuge and strength, a very present help in trouble." This psalm takes us into calamitous times, of mountains being carried into the sea, of earthquakes and tsunamis. Yet in verse 4 we return to "a river whose streams shall make glad the city of God" and in verse 5 we discover that "God is in the midst of her." There is nothing to fear.

Revelation 22 speaks of "a pure river of water of life, clear as crystal, proceeding from the throne of God and the Lamb." On the banks of this river grows the tree of life, which bears 12 fruits, and bears them every month. This tree heals the nations. It is noteworthy that it bears its fruit monthly.

One time I was in Zambia at the Mwami Adventist Mission Hospital, close to the Malawi border. The people speak Chichewa, as do their fellow tribesmen in Malawi. They belong to the Ngoni people, and the paramount chief holds his court a few miles from the hospital.

It was late in the season, before the harvest. On the children's ward were 45 youngsters about 2 years old who had Kwashiorkor disease. This disease often targets 2-year-olds as their mothers may have fed them breast milk until the birth of the next sibling. Lactation will suppress ovulation for many months, but eventually, the ovulatory cycle breaks through the suppressing effect of prolactin, and a woman can become pregnant. With the birth of the new baby, the 2-year-old has to be fully weaned. When weaning coincides with the pre-harvest scarcity of food, protein and calories are in scarce supply.

These little 2-year-olds are not accomplished foragers. Not eating quickly enough, they lose out to the older brothers and sisters who devour any available food. With increasing lethargy, these children become weaker, anemic, low in serum protein, swollen, listless, apathetic, and wasted. They move little, following one's movement with heavy eyes. Tiny ankles are swollen and appear fat. They have potbellies distended with fluid, and are flabby because of flaccid muscles. A casual observer could be tricked into thinking they are fat. However, the distended belly, wasted buttocks, and thin reddish hair all shout malnutrition.

I remember looking at the thin maize-meal gruel these children were being served. "Where is the milk?" I asked. "The government takes all the donated milk from the U.S.A. and Canada and sells it to us, but we have no money to buy it."

I was perplexed, so took a walk to the market to buy beans. The stalls were nearly empty. "No beans. They are all gone. Next month, we will have them, when the harvest comes."

No beans, so I bought the tiny dried fish called kapenta instead. They were revolting wizened little things, with tiny eyes, fins, and scales, dried into their death-contorted form. I took them to the kitchen where they were stewed into a paste. A little spoonful on each child's plate provided the necessary protein, and the children began to recover.

What a delight that the tree of life, watered by the pure river of life that flows from the throne of God and the Lamb, bears its fruit *every month*—a consistent supply. It will never run out.

Such spiritual water continually and perpetually washes away our sins, cleaning our heart and soul, that we may receive the gift of the Holy Spirit. Baptized and washed in the waters of baptism, our sins forgiven beneath the waters of life that flow from Jesus, our lives are taken over by the Holy Spirit. This new birth, described by Jesus to Nicodemus (John 3:5-8), is the passport to heaven. "Unless one is born of water and the Spirit he cannot enter the kingdom of God" (NASB), says Jesus.

Of course, the water is symbolic, but of our belief. Jesus is recorded in Mark 16:16 saying, "He who believes and is baptized will be saved; but he who does not believe will be condemned."

Paul tells us, "But without faith it is impossible to please Him, for he who comes to God must believe that He is, and that He is a rewarder of those who diligently seek Him" (Heb. 11:6).

Baptism signifies this belief. It is an immersion in water that we may be buried as the "old man" and reborn into the newness of life. Water has the ability to saturate and soak, to permeate and pervade substances susceptible to its effects. The water of the earth saturates and enlivens what would otherwise be dry, dead, and dusty.

It is estimated that there are 326 million cubic miles of water on earth. One cubic mile represents more than a trillion gallons of water. Understanding a trillion is not easy. Perhaps it is easier to envision in time. A million seconds is approximately 11½ days. A billion seconds is approximately 31½ years. A trillion seconds is some 31,000 years.

This helps us comprehend the enormity of the world's water, but the interesting thing is to consider where the water is.

The oceans have about 321 million cubic miles of water. The ice caps have about 5.8 cubic miles of water. But saturating the earth, are another 5.6 cubic miles of water (Glick, P.H., 1996: Water Resources, *Encyclopedia of Climate and Weather*, Oxford University Press, vol. 2, pp. 817-823).

All life on the planet contains 269 cubic miles of water.

When I considered this last fact and thought of every tree, shrub, blade of grass, animal, bird, or insect, and that there was more than 1½ million times more water on the earth than was used by all living creatures, I thought of the incredible nature of God. In likening His grace, His power, His capacity to love to water, He assures us of the superabundance of His provision.

Just as the waters of the earth saturate the oceans, earth, atmosphere, rivers, and lakes, His grace and love saturate the universe.

Sometimes we, like the uncomprehending multitude, do not realize the majesty of Jesus. Every step of our journey, He nurtures us. As the Israelites went through the wilderness, He provided water from the rock. He knows our need of water, but we often do not realize our need of His grace, His love, His power—His water of life.

The realization of God's bounty to us will call forth in us a life of praise. Our hearts will thrill to the joy of His indwelling Spirit. The fruit of the Spirit will blossom and flourish in our lives, and we will become a blessing to others.

But it is not only in the spiritual realm we praise the Lord. It is with our whole being—our heart and mind, our whole soul—that we praise. Living praise means paying attention to all aspects of our lives. Living praise means we have not only His spiritual water, but that we use the pure, clean water He has promised for our physical lives to His honor and to His glory.

THE LIQUID OF LIFE

While biological water is but a small fraction of the world's water, our bodies are largely composed of water. In the following we will examine the role of water in our physical health, and will bear in mind that for us to be living praise to God, we need to keep ourselves as healthy as possible.

By weight a newborn infant is approximately 75 percent water, while an adult is approximately 70 percent water. In the body of a 198-pound (90-kilogram) man are approximately 138.6 pounds (63 kilograms) of water. The gray matter of the brain is approximately 85 percent water, blood is approximately 83 percent water, muscles are approximately 75 percent water, and even hard marrow bones are 20 to 25 percent water.[1] Water is essential for the function of every cell of the body. Almost every cell and tissue of our body not only contains water but is continually bathed in fluid and requires water to perform its functions!

Water, the liquid of life, is a

- medium in which metabolism takes place

- transport system within the body

- lubrication for movement

- facilitator of digestion

- waste disposer through the kidneys

- temperature regulator

- major constituent of the circulating blood

About two thirds of ingested water is liquid, and about one third is consumed as food. A small amount is synthesized during food metabolism. Ideally, the body maintains a balance between the amount of water lost each day and the amount taken in to replace it. The daily loss of water depends on climatic conditions and our activities as shown in the following table:

Daily Loss of Water in ml (milliliters) Per Day From an Average Human Body

	Normal Temperature	Prolonged Heavy Exercise
Insensible (from the skin)	350	350
Insensible (from the lungs)	350	650
Sweat	100	5,000
Feces	100	100
Urine	1,400	500
Total output	2,300	6,600

This table shows that sweat is excreted 50 times more when you are on prolonged heavy exercise compared to nonactivity in normal temperature (5,000 ml versus 100 ml). We can see that the average human excretes about 2,300 ml of water daily at normal temperature, and 6,600 ml in prolonged heavy exercise.[2]

What happens to the body when water intake is inadequate? Though the body attempts to conserve water, it continues to lose some through breathing, through the skin, through urine, and the stool.

Excessive loss of water impairs the vital functions of the body, to compensate for the loss, our bodies decrease sweating and urination.

Dehydration results in:

- impairment of body cooling mechanisms with possible temperature elevation

- inefficient clearance of body waste

- increased concentration of the blood, as reflected in higher hematocrit (HCT) value

The percentage of the blood composed of cells is called the hematocrit (an HCT normal value is 42)[3]. If the HCT value is more than 50, the risk of cardiovascular events in men and women increases.[4] Blood viscosity plays a role in hemodynamics; lower blood pressure and lower blood viscosity work together to decrease the risk of stroke.[5]

An increased reabsorption of water from the colon concentrates the stool. This can result in constipation (the most common gastrointestinal complaint in the U.S., causing about 2 million annual visits to the doctor).

Constipation, though influenced by exercise and fiber intake, is also very much reduced by adequate fluid intake. Most people treat themselves without seeking medical help, as evidenced by the US$725 million that Americans spend on laxatives each year.[6]

Dehydration may cause a person to experience dizziness or headache. In this setting analgesics do not address the cause of the headache; more water is required. In the situation of prolonged arduous exercise, serious dehydration may occur. Careful attention to fluid intake is required under these circumstances.

ADVANTAGES OF DRINKING WATER

Drinking adequate water is advocated to reduce the risks of the formation of renal and gallstones.[7, 8] Many studies have been published on the subject of hemorheology[9, 10, 11, 12] (blood flow characteristics) and its impact on a variety of diseases. These indicate that drinking adequate water combined with other aspects of a healthful lifestyle may prevent a variety of diseases. The *Journal of the American Medical Association* called attention to the particular hazards facing older Americans from inadequate fluid intake.[13] It is estimated that if older people would drink sufficient water it could save thousands of days of hospitalization and millions of dollars each year. Such an observation has implications for all age groups.

Dr. Mervyn Hardinge reports a classic experiment conducted by Dr. Pitts at Harvard University that demonstrates the impact of water intake on athletic performance.[14]

In the first test the athletes were instructed to walk for as long as they could on a treadmill at 3.5 miles per hour, without drinking any water. Within three and a half hours, body temperatures rose above 102 degrees, with the athletes reaching the zone of exhaustion. At such high temperatures physiologic functions are impaired, and unless remedied, collapse ensues.

In the second test the same athletes were allowed to drink as much water as they desired. Under these circumstances it took six hours to reach the danger zone of exhaustion. Dr. Pitts discovered that these athletes drank one-third less water than the amount they lost in their sweat. In other words the amount of water that they actually needed equaled their desire plus one-third more.

On the third test the same athletes "forced" water, drinking as much as they had in the previous second test plus the extra volume they were losing in their sweat. With this intake, their body temperature never reached 101 degrees. The experiment was terminated at the end of seven hours, though the athletes felt that they could continue walking indefinitely.

This and other studies show that thirst is not always a reliable indicator of how much water our bodies need. A practical guide to water intake is to consume enough water from the moment you awake in the morning and in between meals throughout the day, to ensure that your urine is clear and diluted. (Note: urine will be bright yellow after taking vitamin pills containing riboflavin, because of the excretion of riboflavin.)

It is preferable to begin drinking water upon awakening, because our bodies are relatively dehydrated from invisible loss of water during sleep. And it is preferable to drink water at regular intervals throughout the day instead of trying to drink a large amount at one time.

It's important to keep your drinking water safe from bacterial contamination. Water is the finest liquid we can consume because it is relatively free of electrolytes and diuretic agents such as caffeine (e.g., tea, coffee). Alcoholic drinks—apart from their other deleterious effects—are a diuretic agent. Most soft drinks are loaded with sugar, contributing to problems of obesity, diabetes, and dental caries. Sugar-free soft drinks carry other risks.

Hydrotherapy—the use of water to treat physical problems—is a simple therapy that few people even know about. But instead of going to a doctor for simple muscular aches, pains, and bruises, try hydrotherapy.

For sore or aching muscles, soak a hand towel or other cloth in hot water, wring it out, and place it on the affected area. When the hot towel cools, replace it with a cold one (a towel soaked in icy water, then wrung dry). Alternate hot and cold, ending with cold. This improves blood flow and promotes healing. The hot and cold fomentations can be repeated several times a day.

In situations in which recent injury and bruising have occurred, use cold compresses. Of course, be very careful if the skin is diseased or cut. If blood flow to the area is compromised or if there is nerve damage, be extremely careful with hot applications. This is especially important in persons with diabetes, for high heat can badly burn the skin and the person may not realize it.

There are many other modes of hydrotherapy too, such as cold mitten friction, hot foot baths, heating compresses, and ice compresses. You can find more information in books and on the Internet.

It is unfortunate that so few utilize this useful tool for relief. A man injured his elbow during a badminton game. Someone suggested an ice cold compress on the bruise and swelling to decrease the internal bleeding, but he wouldn't have it. The next day the bruised area around his elbow was so painful and swollen that he went to see a doctor right away. The doctor advised the home use of ice compresses—and charged a $100 consultation fee!

"The external application of water is one of the easiest and most satisfactory ways of regulating the circulation of the blood. . . . But many have never learned by experience the beneficial effects of the proper use of water. All should become intelligent in its use in simple home treatments."[15]

Obviously, an important use of water is in cleansing our bodies. Bathing removes accumulated dirt and contaminating debris, reducing the risk of infection. Of course, how frequently we bathe may be determined by the availability of water.

Frequent hand washing reduces the transfer of germs from one person to another. In fact, a large percentage of infectious disease would be eliminated if people thoroughly washed their hands with soap and water before eating or after activities that soil their hands, including shaking hands with a large number of people.

RESPONSIBLE USE OF WATER

In addition to the use of water to hydrate our bodies, keep us clean, and prevent disease, we suggest the following as appropriate concerns for earth's inhabitants—that's you and me.

1. **Avoid wasting water.** Some ways this may be accomplished are flushing toilets with smaller amounts of water, using water-conserving shower heads, reducing the amount of water used in bathtubs, turning off leaky taps, and repairing leaking faucets. Think of appropriate ways to conserve water in your own situation.

2. **Avoid polluting water.** Water is polluted by human excrement, industrial waste, and chemicals. Large "feed lot" operations not only have potential to pollute water, but consume large quantities of water in producing meat. Vegetarians, therefore, conserve water, as a plant-based diet requires less water to produce food.

Life cannot exist without water. All body functions require it. It cleanses, refreshes, and powerfully aids the body's restoration. Similarly, in our spiritual lives, we cannot live eternally without the Water of Life.

How about you? Do you too long for that water?

Ellen White counsels, "Those who treat the sick should move forward in their important work with strong reliance upon God for His blessing to attend the means which He has graciously provided, and to which He has in mercy called our attention as a people, such as pure air, cleanliness, healthful diet, proper periods of labor and repose, and the use of water" (*Counsels on Diet and Foods*, p. 303).

"The priest had that morning performed the ceremony which commemorated the smiting of the rock in the wilderness. That rock was a symbol of [Jesus] who by His death would cause living streams of salvation to flow to all who are athirst. Christ's words were the water of life. There in the presence of the assembled multitude He set Himself apart to be smitten that the water of life might flow to the world.

"In smiting Christ, Satan sought to destroy the Prince of Life, but from the smitten rock there flowed living water. As Jesus thus spoke to the people, their hearts thrilled with a strange awe, and many were ready to exclaim with the woman of Samaria, 'Give me this water, that I thirst not!'" (John 4:15) (*The Desire of Ages*, p. 454).

---

[1] M. G. Hardinge, *A Philosophy of Health* (School of Health, 1980), p. 37.

[2] A. C. Guyton, J. E. Hall, *Textbook of Physiology* (W. B. Saunders Co., 2000), p. 265.

[3] *Ibid.*, p. 150.

[4] R. H. Grimm, Jr., J. D. Neaton, W. Ludwig, "Prognostic importance of the white blood cell count for coronary, cancer, and all-cause mortality," *JAMA*, Oct. 11, 1985; 254(14): pp. 1932-1937.

[5] *Ibid.*

[6] my.webmd.com/content/article/1680.52673.

[7] E. Braunwald, A. S. Fauci, et al., editors, *Harrison's Principles of Internal Medicine* (New York: McGraw Hill, Inc., Health Professions Division, 2001), pp. 1616, 1617.

[8] M. V. Math, "Drinking water to prevent gallstone formation," *Gastroenterology,* Apr. 1982; 82(4); pp. 822, 823.

[9] F. J. Nordt, "Hemorheology in cerebrovascular disease: approaches to drug development," *Annals of the New York Academy of Sciences,* 1983; 416: pp. 651-661.

[10] J. Stuart, "Erythrocyte rheology," *Journal of Clinical Pathology,* Sep. 1985; 38(9): pp. 965-977.

[11] G. D. Lowe, "Blood rheology in general medicine and surgery," *Baillieres Clinical Haematology,* Sep. 1987; 1(3): pp. 827-861.

[12] J. Stuart, M. W. Kenny, "Blood rheology," *Journal of Clinical Pathology,* May 1980; 33(5): pp. 417-429.

[13] A. D. Weinberg, K. L. Minaker, "Dehydration. Evaluation and Management in Older Adults," Council on Scientific Affairs, American Medical Association, *JAMA,* Nov. 15, 1995; 274(19): pp. 1552-1556.

[14] G. C. Pitts, R. E. Johnson, F. C. Conzolazio, "Work in the heat as affected by intake of water, salt, and glucose," *American Journal of Physiology,* 142: 253, 1944.

[15] Ellen G. White, *The Ministry of Healing,* p. 237.

CHAPTER 5

THE ENVIRONMENT AND PRAISE

There was a time when meadows, grove, and stream,
The earth, and every common sight,
To me did seem
Appareled in celestial light . . .
The glory and the freshness of a dream.
It is not now as it hath been of yore.
— "Intimations of Immortality," William Wordsworth

E Is for Environmenemt—the Empowerment of Our Communuty
Unfortunately, it would be hard to tell today's industrial tycoons that everything on earth belongs to the Lord! The OPEC cartel certainly doesn't act that way, and the major oil companies are not about to relinquish ownership of all the oil to God or anyone else!

Biological research corporations have experimented with the human genome in an attempt to get patents on snippets of DNA as though they owned the very blueprints of life!

People who believe in the theory of evolution attribute the universe to chance, Planet Earth to a simple condensation of molten material, and life as a spontaneous, random collusion of carbon, hydrogen, and oxygen. Biodiversity is seen as a mindless, yet necessary filling of a vacuum in the ecological niche. Exploration of other planets reveals barren landscapes, lifeless and empty. Obviously, chance did not smile so productively elsewhere! And with an avaricious sense of entitlement, many of us rape the earth with no regard for its welfare or productivity. Mindless consumerism and selfish gratification have already scarred the environment with indelible fingerprints of grasping greed.

The Bible paints the picture of a loving Creator who spent five days of preparation, crafting the perfect environment for us, His special children. Designing the Garden of Eden on the sixth day, God gave protection and comfort to Adam and Eve. Placing them in an exquisite garden, God gave them stewardship of His earthly creatures. Then even though God had supplied every need of our first parents, even though their every want was fulfilled, and even with God Himself visiting them every evening, the desire for more crept into the thoughts of Eve. When the serpent told her that by tasting the forbidden fruit she would become like God, she didn't resist. She had "almost" everything—why not have it all?

Ever since, the human race has wanted more. Insatiable in its desire, even too much is never enough.

Cursed because of sin, the environment became hostile. Thorns grew on vines, rose bushes, and acacia trees. Briars now tangled among flowers. Now Adam's muscles ached from physical toil, and sweat dripped from his brow. The earth, the beautiful earth which once was nurtured and blessed, is now seen as a burden from which resources must be drawn and exploited.

Shifting land masses, altered water courses, and pollution left its mark on the earth, but in the whole course of human history, Planet Earth has never been under siege as it is today. The Industrial Revolution, though raising the standard of living of many, exacted a price that can never be repaid.

The book of Genesis describes the majesty of the Lord. No human-crafted god, His word moves energy, condenses electrons and neutrons, coagulates the elements into chemical bonds that intimidate us in their complexity. Mountains rise, oceans form, rivers flow, trees burst forth, birds fly, beasts roam. The power of His oratory paints the spectrum of color on the flashing wings, the gliding fins and scales. Awesome, this only God, our Creator, whose word is pure power and energy.

But then, with tenderness, with exquisite care, we see the Orator become the Sculptor. The blend of scientist and artistry is incomprehensible to things created, but the sculptor God forms a man of the dust of the ground. Then, with the gentlest kiss of the lover that He is, God breathes His own breath, the life-giving force of His being, into this human form, and man becomes a living soul. Pleased with His work, the sculptor God turns surgeon God, and creates a woman from the living flesh so recently enlivened. As the pair stand before Him, God commissions them as His stewards. Placing them at the peak of the created world, He gives them the pleasure of exploration, and plants curiosity within their brain. Theirs is the world—to be examined, employed, studied. God wants them to come to an appreciation of Himself through the examination of His handiwork. He knows that if they seek, they will find that:

"The heavens declare the glory of God;
and the firmament shows His handiwork.
Day unto day utters speech,
and night unto night reveals knowledge.
There is no speech nor language
where their voice is not heard.
Their line has gone out through all the earth,
and their words to the end of the world" (Ps. 19:1-4).

Not only will humans find the most intricate balance at a micromolecular level, their Hubble telescope will probe the eternity of His creation. But there are some who, without comprehension, babble all kinds of theories in an attempt to explain how all this came about. Not understanding God's loving nature, in their illiteracy many cannot comprehend God's second book—nature.

God knew that left without guidance humans can rapidly devolve into sin. So the Creator God, in His final act of creation—the seventh and perhaps most meaningful act for humans—provided a day of rest.

This day, which the Bible calls Sabbath, is an environment of tranquility. When observed, it becomes a day of restoration, a peace that revives, an antidote for the pollution of sin. It rejuvenates. It brings families together. And it offers a time for personal reflection, meditation, and rest that becomes a buffer against the endless demands of life.

Driven as we can be by avarice and greed, the daily grubbing to acquire ever more, we need to pause and contemplate the real meaning of life. We fill our houses with stuff. We pack our garages with the overflow, then rent storage units to handle even more! Somehow, we're never satisfied. Yesterday's state-of-the-art becomes obsolete in the face of today's cutting edge, which is already shadowed by the promise of tomorrow. Like Eve, many of us live in a virtual paradise, but we are vaguely dissatisfied. The weekly day of rest gives us time to stop. To call out *Enough!* To look once more at the beauty all around that we have grown too accustomed to.

The Sabbath is a day for thanksgiving. God knows that we need to stand back, pause, and take time to breathe in the beauty of life.

But instead of relishing this gift of time, many have tried to embellish it with rules and laws. Not appreciating its true meaning, the Pharisees burdened the Sabbath with seemingly endless regulations. If we spent each Sabbath as a true memorial of creation—as a celebration of our natural environment—we would value far more than we do the pristine blessing of nature.

Creation bears within it the fingerprints of God. But so many of us fail to see them, so busy we are pursuing our own agenda.

One late winter day I watched my backyard from the kitchen window. The trees were bare, the sky was blue. The temperature was in the low 50s. My wife had replenished the feeders, and four squirrels ran around, hopping up onto their feed-block and yo-yoing up and down on its bungee cord support. Cardinals lent flashes of crimson to the silent woods. My gaze went to the bird feeders where small juncos ate hungrily and chickadees swept in on undulating flight paths. A Carolina wren pecked at the suet block while a red-bellied woodpecker clung upsidedown on another suet feeder. The scene was so restful, so beautiful. I felt God's creation infusing me with peace. The phone rang. It was our youngest, now an adult, telling of his Sabbath. He described the sermon in detail; obviously, he had listened. "The foundation of my faith," he said, "is the fact that I believe in a God who sustains and holds the whole world in His hands."

Of all the people in the world, none should care for the earth any more than those who believe it is God's handiwork.

I remember as a 19-year-old, returning from Africa to London. The African skies had always been filled with light. It was hard to exist in London's short, drab winter days. To my photon-deprived brain was added yet another problem—when I blew my nose, my white handkerchief turned black. The air was full of soot. I had seen the heavy pea-soupers of the early 50s. I remember one day the smog was so thick that my parents lost sight of each other though they were only five feet apart. They had to call out to find each other. More than 4,000 people died during those smog-filled years. Coal-burning fires warmed the houses, but polluted the atmosphere. The smog blurred everything. Cars could not move safely. Trees, plants, flowers, houses—all were blotted out with pollution.

Unless we are careful stewards, we are in danger of blotting out so much of creation. It is only a willing ignorance that can deny the dreadful impact our slavish, selfish greed is costing the earth.

Billions of tons of fossil fuels are consumed each year, and the waste pollutes the atmosphere. Around our cities garbage collects like mountains, yet we press thoughtlessly on with our need for more stuff.

It is comforting to look for a new heaven and earth, but if we cannot learn to take care of the earth we have now, what hope is there that we'll be able to steward the new one? Certainly, the pollution of sin will be removed then, but must we always live in expectation of tomorrow? What about today?

Yes, God provided earth's environment for *us*, but it must be protected. Let's consider earth's environment and its implications for our health.

Throughout history civilizations have flourished only where there was a habitable climate, rich soil, and pure water. The physical, chemical, and biotic factors that surround us (think air, temperature, soil, sun, plants, trees, and water) determine our potential health and even our survival.

In other words, people need a sound and healthful environment in order to live. With that simple fact in mind, let's look at some of the issues that will determine our quality of life for years to come. Just as prevention is the best policy for our own health, so prevention is the best policy for our environment. It's much easier to harm the environment than it is to repair it. It's not easy to restore polluted water, denuded forests, toxic air, and contaminated soils. Without sunshine, clean air, soil, and water, the human race cannot survive. We should celebrate the gift of a life-giving environment and do all we can to restore and protect it.

Health-conscious people will take care of their environment for they know it contributes to their health, but unfortunately we're surrounded by pollutants. We can hardly get away from tobacco smoke, automobile emission, industrial waste, smoke from burning grasslands, old, dirty oil, open dump garbage, and sewage pumped into rivers and oceans. But, of course, none of these pollutants *needs* to be part of our environment. There are numerous ways to handle them. It's important to remember that the community's attitude toward pollution begins with the individual. It begins with you.

Without fresh air, clean water, and sunshine, our health suffers. In extreme circumstances, our very survival is threatened.

BENEFITS OF SUNLIGHT

All life on earth depends on the energy of the sun. Without sunshine, life would cease. Sunlight is composed of many different energy levels, transmitted in the form of electromagnetic waves. The sun's rays expose us to three types of light of different wavelengths:

- Invisible light. Ultraviolet light provides the majority of the biological effects, both positive and negative, to our health (5 percent of the solar radiation). Infrared light provides warmth (54 percent of the solar emissions)

- Visible light (40 percent of the solar radiation)

- Shorter cosmic rays, gamma rays, X-rays, longer radio waves, and electromagnetic waves constitute the rest.[1]

Sunshine in appropriate amounts is good for us, but too much puts us at risk for skin damage and skin cancer. However, plants cannot live without sunlight, for they require solar energy to make carbohydrates.

1. *Sunshine helps maintain the existing temperatures of our planet.* In this way it supports both plant and animal life, and is a vital ingredient in our environment.

2. *Plants require sunlight for photosynthesis,* a system of transforming carbon dioxide and water into oxygen, forming organic substances such as vitamins, proteins, carbohydrates, fats, and fiber.

3. *Sunlight produces vitamin D.* Sunlight converts cholesterol derivatives in the skin (cholecalciferol) into vitamin D^2, which is then absorbed into the bloodstream.

The synthetic version of vitamin D comes from the irradiation of vegetable oils with ultraviolet light.[3] Sunlight helps in the building and repairing of the bones by increasing the level of vitamin D in the body. And through exposure to sunlight the body's absorption of calcium is increased, helping prevent rickets and osteomalacia.[4]

People who don't live near the equator, people whose customs and culture require covering their entire bodies, and invalids and infants who are insufficiently exposed to the sun—all require vitamin D supplementation. This necessity highlights the importance of getting vitamin D in your diet.

People who can rely on sunlight for their vitamin D conversion require at least five minutes per day of exposure to the face and hands. Dark-skinned people require six times more exposure to sunshine to produce an equivalent amount of vitamin D than do light-skinned people. People who live where the sunlight is intense should avoid the midday sun. Their best time for exposure to the sun is in the earlier morning hours or the late afternoon.

4. *Sunlight kills many bacteria, viruses, and molds.* If a petri dish in which bacteria have been grown is half covered and the other half exposed to direct sunlight, the covered part of the dish will swarm with bacteria. However, the half exposed to sunlight will show no growth at all. The sunlight will have killed the bacteria.

Opening your curtains and windows to allow sunlight to enter your rooms will help destroy bacteria lurking in the dust. Glass filters much of the ultraviolet light and removes the risk of sunburn. When you're building a house, you have the opportunity to create a home with plenty of ventilation and sunlight. "Let there be a current of air and an abundance of light in every room. . . . No room is fit to be occupied as a sleeping room unless it can be thrown open daily to the air and sunshine."[5]

5. *Sunlight and cancer.* H. G. Ainsleigh observed that it appears the link between exposure to the sun and decreased death rates from certain cancers is due to the ability of vitamin D and related compounds to suppress the abnormal growth of certain cancers.[6] Reported rates of prostate cancer increase as the population moves into northern climes. It is not yet certain whether this is related to sun exposure.

6. *Sunlight powers the recycling of water.* Evaporation raises clean, distilled water into the air where it condenses into clouds. As rain falls, it washes the air and provides dissolved nitrogen to the soil as well as purified water to replenish streams, rivers, and lakes.

7. *Sunlight influences serotonin production.* Research has found that bright light, as well as sunlight, is associated with increased serotonin production, which may prevent depression and fatigue.[7] Some people are adversely affected by the lack of sunlight. Seasonal affective disorder (SAD) was first described in 1984 by Dr. Norman Rosenthal, a neuropsychiatrist at the National Institute of Mental Health. SAD is regarded as a type of major seasonal depression and has many of the same symptoms as clinical depression: loss of energy, change in appetite, tendency to oversleep, difficulty concentrating, and irritability. Someone who has suffered these symptoms for two consecutive winters, but does not have symptoms of depression during the spring and summer months, probably has SAD.[8]

The cure for SAD is very straightforward: more light during the winter months. Dr. Mark Levy, chair of the San Francisco Foundation for Psychoanalysis, says, "For those with mild cases, 30 minutes of exercise in the morning sun may be all that is needed to keep the winter blues at bay." It is interesting that some 80 years before this disorder was recognized, Ellen White, herself living in a northern climate, stated, "There are but few who realize that, in order to enjoy health and cheerfulness, they must have an abundance of sunlight, pure air, and physical exercise. . . . Clothe your boys and girls comfortably and properly. . . . Then let them go out and exercise in the open air, and live to enjoy health and happiness.[9]

She stated further, "Vigor declines as years advance, leaving less vitality with which to resist unhealthful influences; hence the greater necessity for the aged to have plenty of sunlight and fresh, pure air."[10]

One of the effects of pollution is a depletion of the ozone layers in the atmosphere, allowing the increased intensity of radiation. As a result, the incidence of several varieties of skin cancers has increased.

DANGERS OF TOO MUCH SUN

1. Malignant melanoma. During the past 20 to 30 years the number of people developing malignant melanoma has increased significantly.

Dermatologists encourage wearing broad-brimmed hats and using sunscreens to reduce the effects of ultraviolet light on the skin. Sunscreens come in varying strengths, usually expressed as sun protection factors (SPF). A value more than 30 is recommended. Apply sunscreen before spending long periods in the sun, and reapply frequently as required, for example after swimming. Some sunscreens must be on the skin for several minutes before you get the full benefit, so read the label to make sure. The active ingredient most often used at the time of writing is Parsol 1789.

2. Squamous cell carcinoma. This cancer is increased in individuals living in areas where they are exposed to prolonged sunshine.

3. Basal cell carcinoma. This cancer is similarly increased, especially in light-skinned people that live in the tropics. In all of these conditions, damage to the skin is cumulative, and many children receive solar irradiation that will progress to skin cancer in later life. This underlines the need to protect young children from excessive exposure to sunlight.

THE PROBLEM OF DIRTY AIR

Pollution of the atmosphere is a most significant and serious problem. It will be discussed more fully in the later section on air. It is sufficient to note, however, that carbon dioxide emission is considered to be a major contributor to global warming, which, should it progress, could become a devastating problem to the entire world.

Industrial emissions with their heavy sulfur content have resulted in acid rain. This can destroy vegetation and increase acidity of lakes, resulting in the sterilization of plant and animal life that lives within them.

People who live in heavily industrialized areas have increased respiratory problems such as chronic bronchitis and asthma. It has been noted that young children growing in a smog-polluted atmosphere have a decreased growth rate of their lungs. This can be as much as 1 percent per annum less than that of children growing in a pollution-free environment. In one study that began in 1993, USC researchers selected volunteers from 12 communities within a 200-mile radius of the Los Angeles area. The volunteers consisted of 150 fourth-graders, 75 seventh-graders, and 75 tenth-graders from each community. Each year the children were tested for lung function by measuring how much and how fast they could blow out air.

The researchers found that the lung function growth of children who live in smoggier parts of southern California is lower than those who breathe cleaner air. Children with lower lung function growth are more likely to have chronic respiratory problems in adulthood.[11]

As concerned inhabitants of the world, we need to protect our environment by addressing the issues of deforestation, pollution, energy utilization, water, and waste management. These are practical, everyday issues both for industrialized and developing nations and have a significant impact on our daily lives.

At a personal level how we utilize energy is a critical concern. We should thoughtfully consider the size of our homes and cars and our use of electricity. In a world threatened by the overuse of energy sources, can we in good conscience heat and cool thousands of square feet we don't actually use? And if we actually need all that space, are there other ways we could heat and cool it?

No matter where you live, if it's available and feasible, explore alternative sources of energy such as solar, wind, and water. Our personal environment—our homes—contribute to the overall picture. Simple measures such as switching off a light and raising or lowering thermostat temperatures by one or two degrees can have a significant impact on energy saving as well as on your bill. And think of transportation. More and more communities are putting in sidewalks and bike lanes. Instead of always driving, could we sometimes walk where we need to go? Cooking also often utilizes more energy than required. Think of ways you could conserve energy when you cook.

TOXIC WASTE

Outbreaks of infection often result from water polluted with sewage. Equally serious is the pollution of water supplies with industrial waste such as mercury, lead, and polychlorinated biphenols (PCBs), which result from careless handling of these waste products. Increasingly the water supplies of the world are becoming less suitable for drinking. All citizens should make protection of our water supplies a priority.

The dumping of waste products onto the soil has resulted in serious health problems. Whether the waste is radioactive, old oil, toxic chemicals, or materials that do not decay and biodegrade naturally, the soil is damaged. Problems associated with chemical fertilization and pesticide residues continue to pose challenges to both farmers and environmentalists. Irrigation projects and their associated chemical fertilizers have in many instances resulted in serious alteration of soil composition.

From time to time, in the course of my work-related travel, I have witnessed scenes of human desperation. There are few that distress me more than the sight of human scavengers. When these scavengers are children, it is even more painful. Just two weeks before I penned these words, I watched in anguish as youths foraged through the dirt and detritus of a dumpster in Antananarivo, Madagascar. And a short while back, I saw people combing a massive garbage dump in India. More horrifying was the information that these people *live* on the dump—sleeping there, rearing babies there, and dying there! Scrabbling amid the refuse, their lives seemed reduced to merely trying to stay alive.

What of their hopes? Do they have dreams? Can they have any future at all?

How does the gospel penetrate through such dire need?

Recently such thoughts were heightened and brought into much clearer focus when I read a book by Alan Weisman, *The World Without Us*. The author is obviously an evolutionist, but he describes his vision of what would happen to the earth if humans were to be mysteriously removed from its surface. His scientific background equips him well for his imaginary scenarios, but also permits him to paint a gruesome future if we should *not* disappear from the earth. It is this terrible potential of the entire earth as a giant garbage dump that is horribly compelling. Compelling to me, that Jesus has to come soon, compellingly convincing that we are all part of the pollution problem and that all of us must be part of the solution. It's up to us—all of us—to make the earth a better place to live.

PLASTICS LAST FOREVER

Among the many riveting chapters in Weisman's book is one titled "Polymers Are Forever." Here he describes the work of several marine biologists, including Richard Thompson, who, as an undergraduate, helped clean the shoreline of Britain's west coast. While removing some of the tons of garbage that washed ashore each day, he noted that the larger floating pieces seemed to be directed by the wind. This meant that he was cleaning up trash that had come from Ireland, and that England's floating trash befouled the shores of Scandinavia! Unlike the big floating material, however, was a massive amount of small particulate trash. Often the casual observer does not even notice this among the bottles, plastic bags, automobile tires, pieces of rope, and plastic caps.

Now a professor at Plymouth University, Thompson points out a special subspecies of particle called nurdles that are found in the waters around Plymouth. Shaped like uniform little rods some two millimeters in length, these are the raw materials used to create plastic products of any conceivable shape. These nurdles must have been carried by currents for hundreds of miles, for there are no plastic factories near Plymouth where they are found.

Wave action pounds plastic particles smaller and smaller. (It is this type of particle debris that Thompson's lab studies.) When the particulate debris is analyzed in the lab, one third is found to be biologic debris, one third is clearly particulate plastic, and another third is composed of particles that defy exact definition—but plastic polymers of some kind.

Plastics are largely a post-World War II phenomenon. They have only been around some 70 years.

Early in the twentieth century Alistair Hardy, another marine biologist, began the collection of samples of the sea by means of collecting krill in a special apparatus he designed to be dragged behind ocean-going vessels. The sampling program he started has continued, with stored specimens providing a chronological history of the oceans spanning the last century. The apparatus drags about 10 meters below the surface, collecting tiny shrimp-like creatures called krill. Krill are part of the bedrock layer of the earth's food chain. They ingest tiny particles, and function like microsieves of the ocean.

In the first half of the century plastic was not found in the samples but by the 1960s, it was noted that the krill were ingesting plastic particles. By the 1990s the plastic content in the oceans had tripled.

Now, since most plastic floats, finding it at 10 meters—some 33 feet—below the ocean surface was disturbing. Plastic does not degrade; it only becomes ever smaller, obviously small enough for tiny krill to eat.

We are familiar with pictures of turtles eating plastic bags or birds strangled in plastic or nylon fishing line. But here we have the tiniest of creatures eating microparticulate plastic, often with lethal consequences, for often their guts get plugged with the nondigestible stuff.

It's not news to plastic producers that plastic is not biodegradable. Aware of the mounting mountains of plastic trash, manufacturers developed biodegradable plastic bags made from a mixture of cellulose and plastic. The cellulose breaks down just fine, because it is basically a sugar, and organic—but the plastic parts of the bags remain, only now in microparticulate form, all the more readily washed into the ocean.

CONSUME LESS. CONSERVE MORE.

One night I lay to luxuriate in the tub. I like the relaxation of a warm bath, but having read Weisman's book, I couldn't enjoy it as much for I counted six plastic bottles around the tub's perimeter. There were two kinds of shampoo, two conditioners, one body wash, and one tube of facial cleanser. Across, on the shelf, were plastic containers of intensive care lotion. Then I saw pill bottles—issued a quarter full only three months at a time, to ensure that the pharmacy collected the quarterly copayment. The bathroom garbage container was lined with a plastic bag. My toothbrush is plastic; so is my hairbrush. My travel kit is made of plastic.

Plastic is everywhere! Yet if time continues, these plastic "necessities" will persist as detritus on some sickly shore a hundred or a thousand years from now.

Just think of the millions of plastic bottles used each day by millions of people whose water supply is safe, but—preferring the convenience of a disposable bottle—they "drink it and drop it."

A simple filter can make any American city's water taste as good as any bottled water. Why not a reusable metal flask, refilled at home?

It's probable that we'll never go back to living without plastic, but we must be involved in its recycling. It too has to be made more easily recycled. Currently, it costs more to recycle plastic than to make new—but that's because we're not counting the cost to the earth. Something must change. To start, perhaps, taxes need to favor recycled products.

Plastic has become ubiquitous. In our dainty attempts at hygiene we stoop to scoop, but now—dispensing with the bucket and scoop (they were both plastic anyway)—we encase our pets' natural droppings in a time capsule of plastic. Just imagine Rover's daily "offerings" given "immortality." Our throwaway, disposable society is in such high gear that vast tracks of ocean have become slowly rotating cesspools.

The North Pacific Subtropical Gyre is a 10-million-square-mile ocean dump. (Go to the Internet and look this up. It's an eye-opener!) This slowly gyrating siphon of the Pacific's debris is one of six such systems in the world's oceans. Samples of this floating quagmire show plastic particles outnumber plankton by a factor of more than six times.

Plastic particles in that facial dermabrasive that we use to smooth our skin trickle down the drain into the sewers, and eventually out to sea. Not large enough to be wind driven, they will be carried into the ponderous currents of the deep. Weisman says they will exist forever.

Is it going to end soon? As Adventists, we believe it must!

But in the meantime, while God has commissioned us to be stewards of the earth and occupy it until Jesus comes, small countries such as Kenya produce 4,000 tons of plastic bags *each month*! As for those "nurdles" I mentioned—250 billion pounds of them are produced each year. Quite a lot for an almost-indestructible product! This is the way we act as stewards of the earth? This is how we care for God's creation?

Another problem with particulate marine plastic is its ability to act like a sponge for resilient poisons such as DDT and the toxic polychlorinated biphenols (PCBs). The latter, used to make plastic more pliable, were banned in 1970 because of their toxicity. Still, if given the chance, the pre-1970 flotsam will leak its PCBs for centuries.

Taking samples of the plastic soup the seas are rapidly becoming, scientists discovered that the particulate plastic attracts and concentrates such toxins to one million times their normal occurrence in sea water. Given the propensity of sea creatures to ingest such matter, it is natural to expect such toxins to concentrate in the fat tissue of marine animals.

What about humans? It has been documented that toxic PCBs are now appearing in breast milk! We need to pay attention.

Dr. Tony Andrady, a leading expert on plastic, says "every bit of plastic manufactured in the world for the last 50 years or so, still remains." That is more than one billion tons of the stuff.

"Will you take a paper or plastic bag?" the checkout clerk asks.

"Huh?" you pause. "Oh, the plastic seems easier. Let's save the trees!"

Wrong answer. Ask for a hemp, a cloth, or a paper bag. Better yet, bring your own reuseable bags to the store.

Plastic is only one among the myriads of waste products our consumer world is producing. With spreading industrialization in China and Asia, waste products are accelerating. Just the debris from our obsolete computers is massive. Carbon dioxide is warming the planet as it befouls the atmosphere; radioactive waste that has a half-life of thousands of years is still being produced.

Isn't it time to think seriously about our part in the trashing of the earth? Surely, as custodians of the earth, we need to learn to consume less, conserve more, and care for the handiwork of God.

It's easy to think that one person can't make a difference, so why try? But here's an idea: live "as if." Live *as if* everything you do, everything you buy, everything you use makes a difference. Because it does.

The Bible tells me that God gave human beings "dominion over the fish of the sea, over the birds of the air, and over the cattle, over all the earth and over every creeping thing that creeps on the earth" (Gen. 1:26).

Such dominion surely calls for responsibility and accountability.

Revelation 11:18 speaks of Jesus coming back to destroy those who destroy the earth. When I was a boy, the earth seemed to me so vast, so enormous, it seemed incomprehensible for a puny race of mere people to destroy it. Now, with an ever-expanding population, with industrial proliferation, with "growth," "growth," and "more growth" the mantra of all economies, the destruction of the earth seems all too possible. Even probable. Most of us recognize that the earth is, as the Bible says, growing old like a garment. We also must face the fact that it is we who are wearing it out!

As our planet becomes "shrink-wrapped" in plastic, all life is squeezed and distorted. God must look with horror as the world becomes more and more like a trash heap of pollution. And like in so many other areas of health, having disdained prevention we're frantically searching for a cure.

It might be easy to say, "Oh, Jesus will make it all alright," but I don't want to be one of those who make it all so wrong. Surely we respect God enough to honor His handiwork.

How will we stand in the great judgment day when the review of our stewardship of the earth takes place?

Will we be found guilty of wanton behavior and neglect?

Yet God, in His love and mercy, makes available to all, regardless of their status, an internal atmosphere of peace, joy, and contentment. God gives to all the blessing of life. He makes His sun to rise on the evil and on the good (Matt. 5:45).

"If your voices are uplifted in prayer to heaven for light, the Lord Jesus, who is light and life, peace and joy, will hear your cry. He, the Sun of Righteousness, will shine into the chambers of your mind, lighting up the soul temple."[12]

Exposed to the Sun of Righteousness, our whole life will be illuminated and changed. When we drink of the fountain of life, we will not thirst. When we breathe the atmosphere of heaven, we will be at peace. When we are grounded in the rich soil of biblical truth, we will live a healthful lifestyle, and God will fill our lives with CELEBRATIONS.

Perhaps the words penned by Ellen White more beautifully than ours paint the picture of the perfect environment.

"From the solemn roll of the deep-toned thunder and old ocean's ceaseless roar, to the glad songs that make the forests vocal with melody, nature's ten thousand voices speak His praise. In earth and sea and sky, with their marvelous tint and color . . . we behold His glory. The everlasting hills tell us of His power. The trees that wave their green banners in the sunlight, and the flowers in their delicate bounty, point to their Creator. The living green that carpets the brown earth tells of God's care for the humblest of His creatures. The caves of the sea and the depths of the earth reveal His treasures. . . . The sun rising in the heavens is a representative of Him who is the life and light of all that He has made." (*Ministry of Healing*, pp. 411, 412).

[1] M. G. Hardinge, *Health Series Slide and Video Program*.

[2] L. M. Salamonte, G. E. Dallal, et al., "A contribution of vitamin D intake and seasonal sunlight exposure to plasma 25 hydroxyvitamin D concentration in elderly woman," *American Journal of Clinical Nutrition*, Jan. 1994; 59(1): pp. 80-86.

[3] Dyson Carter, "Synthetic poison [vitamin D^2]," (1945), reprinted in *Townsend Letter for Doctors*, April 1994: pp. 392, 393.

[4] M. F. Holick, M. B. Clark, "The Photobiogenesis and Metabolism of Vitamin D," *Federal Proceedings*, 37 (1978): p. 2567.

[5] Ellen G. White, *The Ministry of Healing*, pp. 274, 275.

[6] H. G. Ainsleigh, "Beneficial effects of sun exposure on cancer mortality," *Preventive Medicine*, Jan. 1993; 22(1): pp.132-140.

[7] M. L. Rao, B. Muller-Oerlinghousen, et al., "The influence of phototherapy on serotonin and melatonin in nonseasonal depression," *Pharmacopsychiatry*, May 1990; 23(3): pp. 155-158.

[8] A. S. Fauci, E. Braunwald, et al., editors, *Harrison's Principles of Internal Medicine* (New York: McGraw Hill, Inc., Health Professions Divisions, 2001), p. 2549.

[9] Ellen G. White, *My Life Today*, p. 138.

[10] Ellen G. White, *The Ministry of Healing*, p. 275.

[11] *American Journal of Respiratory and Critical Care Medicine*, October 2000.

[12] Ellen G. White, *The Adventist Home*, p. 343.

CHAPTER 6

BOLSTERING BELIEF

I have a sin of fear, that when I have spun
My last thread, I shall perish on the shore:
But swear by Thyself that at my death Thy Son
Shall shine as He shines now, and heretofore
And, having done that, Thou hast done:
I shall fear no more.
— *"A Hymn to God the Father," John Donne*

B Is for Belief—the Basis of Our Spirituality

"But without faith, it is impossible to please Him, for he who comes to God must believe that He is, and that He is a rewarder of those who diligently seek Him" (Heb. 11:6).

When we were about to return from Africa, I found I had some money that I was not going to be able to remove from Zimbabwe by reason of the currency control. "Blocked funds," they might be called, so I decided to reward the two men who had been our workers. For James the gardener I put some money in his bank.

For Enoch I took a similar amount, paid some months' salary into a post office account for his wife, and purchased a ticket for him to visit with us in Canada. Enoch had been educated to about a grade three level, and had lived his life in a rural village. He found Canada a very strange and different place. I remember one day in particular. The sun was brilliant, the sky blue, but the outside temperature was minus 15 degrees Celsius. It was so cold, it could freeze your whiskers and they could be snapped off. At least, it felt that way.

Enoch decided he would go for a walk. "I think you should put on a hat," I said.

"No, the sun is shining," he replied. "I won't need a hat."

I raised my eyebrows at Janet, and said, "OK!"

A few minutes later, a shivering and very cold Enoch returned. "Doctor," he said, "when I tell them back home that the sun can shine, but the whole town is a refrigerator, they just will not believe!"

Another time we took him to an amusement park, Canada's Wonderland. He enjoyed the rides with our 8-year-old Danny, and then we came to a contraption called The Bat. I knew from the faint whiff of vomitus in the air that this was not a ride for me, but Danny wanted to go. "Please, Daddy, please!" he begged.

The Bat consisted of two giant tracks that rose perhaps 200 feet into the air, and were connected by a loop. The cars were drawn up the one side, then suddenly released where they raced down to rattle around the loop—accompanied by squeals and shrieks—then shot up the other side. The car then came to a stop—and repeated the devilish ride, this time in reverse.

"Please, Daddy!"

"But you need to be accompanied by an adult," I told him.

"Enoch can come with me, Daddy, can't you Enoch?"

We looked at Enoch. "Sure," he said. "If Danny can do it, so can I."

I watched the two of them. Click, click, click went the car, as it was ratcheted up the track. All stood still then . . . *whoompf!* it let go and down the track it flew. *Vroom!* it went around the loop, *vroom!* and up the other side. I had caught sight of Enoch's eyes—wide and white against his dark skin. I knew his heart rate would be 140. The contraption paused, then *whoompf!* it rocketed back down the track.

The two of them staggered off the platform. Both looked shaken. Enoch's brown skin had a powdered look. He was obviously shook up.

"Doctor," he said, "they will never believe!"

"Who won't believe?" I asked.

"When I tell them back in Zimbabwe that I was taken two kilometers into the sky and dropped down, they will never believe."

"No, Enoch," I said. "They will never believe."

Belief is not always easy. If things are outside the realm of our experience, beyond our value system, or judged irrational, we don't believe. On the other hand, much of what we believe may be irrational to people who have not had our experiences.

Some things are so obviously part of all human experience that we all accept them. Drop a stone from one's hand, and it falls to the ground. We all know that. But drop a stone in a space ship, and it floats. Why?

The world of physics provides a simple explanation, but there are many questions that even the most sophisticated physicists struggle to answer. In some areas we are so used to things that we believe without question. The use of television, computers, iPods, and other electronics beyond the understanding of most of us have conditioned us to believe without any means of verification. Most of us have never seen a stem cell, or even a cell for that matter, but we blindly accept that organs can be grown in the laboratory from such cells. We take injections of a vaccine to protect us from a variety of illnesses, the way they work being quite mysterious to us.

But there are skeptics, people who disagree with the popular opinion of the day—and every now and then they are proven to be correct.

Disagreement becomes much more common when there is no hard, demonstrable evidence. A lot of evidence is not hard, but suggestive—subjective more than objective. Our opinions are a result of our conditioning, and when hypothesis rather than fact forms the basis of our belief, we are floating and carried by currents of which we may be unaware.

So, how do we believe in a God we have not seen, touched, or felt?

Sometimes we become aware of the existence of something by its absence. If we were to examine an electric wall socket, even in the absence of a plug, we could assume there was a need for something like a plug from observing the holes in the socket. If we examine a light bulb attached to a light stand, connected to a plug, and attached to the wall socket, we would guess at some purpose. If we then saw some lamps lighted up and others not, we might assume some force —invisible yet powerful—was somehow at work.

When we see the lives of others illuminated, perhaps changed, we ponder; when we read the life of Jesus, we are confronted by a mysterious happening. Of course, we could pooh-pooh the story of Jesus. We can relegate the Gospels to the realm of fairy tales. However, the disciples lived their lives convicted of His reality and died as martyrs for their convictions. They never wavered in their *belief.* Having spent three years with this man Jesus, they were convinced He had risen from the dead. They were not all credulous simpletons, either. Thomas said, "Unless I put my fingers in the palm prints, and my hand in His side, I will not believe."

They had seen *real* nails, watched a *real* spear perforate His *real* body, and seen *real* blood come from His side. They then believed He was, in reality, raised from the dead. They believed well enough to die for that belief—some to be beheaded, or crucified, or tortured for that belief. So it is very likely that, as Peter said, "We did not follow cunningly devised fables when we made known to you the power and coming of our Lord Jesus Christ, but were eyewitnesses of His majesty" (2 Peter 1:16). They were, in fact, believers of the *reality* of the risen Jesus.

I had a favorite uncle, Uncle Paul, who told wonderful tales to us when we were children. Having become ill with tuberculosis as a boy, he had little formal education. At that time he was taken out of school and lived in a little solarium in the garden, built for him by my grandfather. Someone took food out to him, and he had books to read. He lived one year in such isolation. Later he became a very strong man, and followed the family construction business. He was an able bricklayer, taking great pride in his work. As he aged into his 90s, I became concerned for him and my Auntie Elsie, who lived alone in the little house he had built.

"Uncle Paul," I asked him one day when phoning him from Canada, "What would you say is the most important lesson life has taught you?"

In his Tyneside drawl, he answered, "Allan, the most important lesson is that God is real."

Jesus taught that lesson to His disciples. At the time of the Pentecost, the lesson was reinforced by the coming of the Holy Spirit in a very visible way. The concept of being filled with the Holy Spirit became part of the Christian experience. It was Paul who prayed Romans 15:13, NIV: "May the God of hope fill you with all joy and peace as you trust in him, so that you may overflow with hope by the power of the Holy Spirit."

The words *belief, faith, hope,* and *trust* differ slightly in meaning, but all encompass confident optimism and great expectation.

We don't live in a comfortable world. Economic turmoil, climate change, new diseases, wars, famine, violence—all confirm the presence of evil and, consequently, many doubt the existence of God.

But many fail to actually decide what they believe! Belief in anything is a result of a choice we make to accept as true the issue under consideration. To believe that a Republican form of government is superior to that of the Democrats is a belief that may or may not have consequences. To believe a certain stock will rise or fall may make or lose you money. It's unlikely that believing one make of a car is better than another will make a huge difference in your life. Yet the choices implicit in coming to most beliefs are minor compared to the implications of your choice whether or not to believe in God.

Some of us live our lives in fear or dread. It's possible to conjure up all kinds of disastrous outcomes and consequences. I see even some Christians consumed with anxieties as they look upon the calamitous prospects of life. Some want to run away "to the mountains," to be sequestered from the realities of life. They live as though they can escape this real world into an isolated cocoon. But in his letter to Timothy, Paul tells him, "For God has not given us a spirit of fear, but of power and of love and of a sound mind" (2 Tim. 1:7). We can live in His presence anywhere. Under inspiration, Isaiah wrote, "Fear not, for I am with you; be not dismayed, for I am your God. I will strengthen you, yes, I will help you, I will uphold you with My righteous right hand" (Isa. 41:10).

For those who choose to place their belief, their trust, and their lives in the hands of a loving heavenly Father, life takes on a far more serene and purposeful meaning. It is meaning that calls me most powerfully to God. Were I to accept, as so many believe today, that our existence is an expression of chance, that the carefully interwoven codependence of the ecology is circumstantial, that random events decide our meaning, I would be very afraid. I would be afraid I was missing out by not being a billionaire. I would worry that my life was of so little value I could be killed without remorse or consequence. After all, if I just happen to be here by chance, without meaning, what value do I have other than taking up space? If there is no morality other than what is best for the group—but the whole group exists only by happenstance—what right does one group have over another? Anarchy and exploitation should rule, as indeed they seem to be doing in so many situations. But when I believe that there is an organization, a plan, a design to life, because there is a Designer and Planner and Organizer, then my life and yours become meaningful.

Of course, our ideas of God may differ, change, or waver.

The Bible recounts the experiences of men and women who have believed and been inspired by God. God's guidance of peoples, the gift of prophecy, the redemption by God's love is reiterated again and again, culminating in the life and death of Jesus. The prophecies of Daniel predicted the exact time of Christ's birth. His death and sacrifice on Calvary were all foretold in the prophecies. All these buttressed the belief of the disciples and of Paul.

Two people, walking to Emmaus, have their hearts opened as Jesus explains from Scripture the Messiah's birth, ministry, death, and resurrection. When, at last, they recognize Him and He disappears, they retrace their steps, saying to each other, "Did not our heart burn within us?" Hope and faith come from belief.

The promise is given that, when we seek, we shall find. The Scriptures are packed with stories of ordinary people experiencing an extraordinary God.

Scripture points out the danger of self-made religions or philosophy. Peter emphasizes the fruit of the relationship with Jesus, the obedience, humility, kindness, and purity that is seen in the transformed lives of His followers. Such transformation speaks to the triumph of God's love over the bitter hatred of our natural character. The prophet Jeremiah gave his testimony that "The Lord is good to those whose hope is in him, to the one who seeks him" (Lam. 3:25, NIV).

Yet more than belief is required of the Christian, for Paul said that even the devils believe and tremble. Nahum 1:7, NIV, reads, "The Lord is good, a refuge in times of trouble. He cares for those who trust in him."

Beyond a belief in His existence, the Bible teaches that God is good. In fact, God is defined as love, and millions have experienced His goodness. Much time could be spent wondering what God is like. Because He is beyond our comprehension, it could be argued that theology is only a superficial study and that theologians argue a lot about what they can't possibly know or understand. Regardless of the mysteries of the Godhead, and the questions of His existence in another dimension, it is sufficient to understand Him in the incarnate Jesus. Compassion, caring, love, empathy, and, earnest desire to be in tune with the heavenly Father marked how God would have us be. To be like Jesus is to become more Godlike.

To reach such an understanding of God, we go to the inspiration and insights given to the many prophets of old. What encourages the Bible student most is the integrated closely woven similarity in all that they wrote. The tightly knit presentation of a coming Messiah, the constant theme of redemption, shown in ritual and practice, foreshadowed the life and reality of Jesus Christ. The fulfillment of prophecy—the inexorable unified progress over many centuries, culminating in Jesus—gives Christians faith.

The miracles of healing are an interesting aspect of the Bible. For some who reject out of hand their very possibility, they become major stumbling blocks. For others who accept them, they become an evidence of the supernatural. Schooled in the field of medicine, I am a superskeptic of miracles. But when a man's withered arm is suddenly strong and whole, when a man blind from birth sees; when a leper, with his oozing, scaly skin becomes clean—even I have to admit that these are not psychological events.

You see, it was not Christ who confirmed the miracles He did, but the priests who inspected the skin and who sometimes, to their own chagrin, had to admit a person had been healed. The withered arm that becomes whole is not some imaginary change. The witness of the demoniac, the former grave-dweller and shackled madman, was reasoned, cogent, and coherent enough that the whole town turned out to see Jesus the next time He came that way. It was Jesus who said it is a wicked, adulterous people that need signs before they would believe. He looks for His people to be healthy and happy. Under the dictate of sin in our nature, He wants us free. In the practice of religion, He has embedded blessings that are hard for even the most hardened to explain.

THE BLESSINGS OF HAVING FAITH

Belief or faith in a religious setting has been shown to have statistically significant benefits that exceed the placebo effect. A fascinating study was made that examined the religious experience of Americans who had reached the golden age of 100. Among the centenarians the researchers found that personal religion had significantly enhanced their health. Although there are still many unanswered questions, the benefits of trust in God result from more than simply attending religious services.[1]

An elegant study of secular and religious *kibbutzim* from Israel showed quite clearly a decreased mortality rate during a 15-year follow-up in the religious group. The age-adjusted risk ratio of being members of the secular *kibbutz* was 1.8 for males and 2.7 for females.[2] The religious group had one half of this mortality risk.

It is interesting that the far-reaching benefits of faith transcend age and racial boundaries. A recent study of African-Americans found that those who engaged in organized religious activities had improved health and life satisfaction.[3] Similarly, C. G. Ellison, writing in *Social Science and Medicine,* found that a lack of religious affiliation increases the risk of depression in African-Americans.[4]

A connection between social relationships and survival has been documented in several studies. V. J. Schoenbach, et al., have documented this effect particularly among White males.[5] One of the most consistant findings across all racial groups is that spirituality profoundly improves the quality of life. The profound benefits in the quality of life brought about by exercising faith are described by a Duke University researcher as follows:[6]

- Religious attendance and private devotion strengthen a person's religious belief system.

- Strong religious systems, in turn, when accompanied by a high level of religious certainty, have a substantial and positive influence on well-being.

- Individuals with strong religious faith report higher levels of life satisfaction, greater personal happiness, and fewer negative psychosocial consequences of traumatic life events.

Another amazing aspect of spirituality is that it not only helps believers but also benefits the nonbelievers in their community. Research demonstrates that communities actually gain health benefits when they have higher numbers of adherents to faiths that emphasize implicit obedience to God and His standards of conduct.[7] Probably the reason that nonbelievers are benefitted as well is that their social norms favor conformity to the more healthful lifestyle embraced by their more religious neighbors.

Religious people, particularly adolescents from religious homes who frequently attend religious services, pray, and read Scripture have fewer problems with alcohol, tobacco, or other drugs than do their nonreligious peers.[8]

Researchers also found that religion was positively associated with emotionally healthful values and socially accepted behavior, such as tutoring or other volunteer activity often promoted by their religious organization.[9]

Harold G. Koenig, M.D., discusses the findings of Idler and Kasl. These reporters noted a connection between healthier emotional lives and closer social ties in religiously active people, which often resulted in lower levels of disability. The increased physical activity associated with leisure and social activities did not fully account for the increased benefits in these people's lifestyle, and the authors concluded, "A significant effect of religiousness remains even after social activities have been considered."[10]

We see that belief in a loving God is a positive and powerful health-promoting state of mind. There is nothing more reassuring than the peace and satisfaction experienced by those who place their lives in the hands of a loving God and who are aware of His love for them. This brings health, happiness, and a sense of purpose. A belief in God may be associated with reduction in stress, depression, and loneliness.

A 1990 Gallup poll revealed that more than 36 percent of Americans live with chronic feelings of loneliness. According to a Princeton University Research Associates survey, at least two thirds of Americans feel stressed-out at least once a week. Stress, loneliness, and related depression can have serious consequences. Somewhere between 75 and 90 percent of all doctor visits contain components relating to stress.[11]

Medical science has discovered that when you feel stressed out from facing challenges, the negative emotions trigger the release of certain hormones and stimulate the nervous system in such a way as to put stress on the various organs of the body. If subjected to stress over long periods of time, these organs become weakened and thus are more susceptible to a variety of disease processes. The order and intensity with which organs are affected depend upon the person's heredity, constitution, environment, and lifestyle. For example:

- Stress may cause the release of adrenaline, making the heart beat more rapidly and powerfully. Such stress may cause one to suffer from heart palpitations (unpleasant awareness of heartbeat).

- When stress hormones cause the blood vessels to constrict, they may augment the effects of hypertension and cause diminished peripheral vascular flow, leading to cold hands and feet.

- Stress may induce shallow and rapid breathing with bronchial dilation, which causes hyperventilation and tetany.

- Stress results in diversion of the blood supply away from the digestive system, possibly affecting digestive processes.

- Stress induces a state of increased clotting of the blood which, though protective in some circumstances, could have deleterious effects in others.

- Chronic stressful conditions may increase perspiration, leading to unpleasant dampness.

- Stress causes an increase in blood glucose (to serve as a rapid source of energy); in the diabetically predisposed, chronic stress may lead to the hastening of the onset or exacerbation of diabetes mellitus.

- Stress may cause alterations in gastrointestinal and urinary functions. Some may suffer from urinary frequency and irritable bowel syndrome.

A stressed person may visit the doctor for numerous physical complaints and may suffer from emotional disorders such as anxiety, depression, phobias, cognitive disorders, memory problems, and sleep disorders.

THE ASTOUNDING POWER OF PRAYER

In an Ohio study[12] regarding the effects of prayer on well-being, there were altogether 560 respondents, 95 percent of whom classified themselves as religious people. Fifty-four percent were Protestants and 25 percent Catholics. Using factor analysis, researchers were able to identify four types of prayer, namely:

- Petitional prayer; praying to God for material things you may need

- Ritual prayer; praying to God by reading the book of prayers

- Meditative prayer; praying to God by "feeling" or being in His presence

- Colloquial prayer; praying to God as talking to a friend and asking Him for guidance in making decisions

Of all these types of prayer, the study revealed that colloquial prayer correlates best with happiness and religious satisfaction; whereas, ritual prayer is associated with a negative effect and feeling all the more sad, lonely, tense, and fearful. Talking to God as to a friend, telling Him all our joys and sorrows, can bring happiness, healing, and religious satisfaction. So important is the role of prayer in healing that Dr. Larry Dossey stated, "I decided that *not* to employ prayer with my patients was the equivalent of withholding a potent drug or surgical procedure."[13]

Many people have tried to solve their problems through yoga or some similar internalized program of self-empowerment; however, these methods do not have the same effectiveness. Dr. Freda Morris, former professor of medical psychology at the University of California Los Angeles, points out that in many cases these programs are really techniques of self-hypnosis.

The Bible says, "You will keep him in perfect peace, whose mind is stayed on you, because he trusts in you" (Isa. 26:3). When we have a close relationship with God, we experience peace of mind.

This does not mean that our lives will be exempt from problems. "Trouble and turmoil may surround us, yet we enjoy a calmness and peace of mind of which the world knows nothing. This inward peace is reflected in a . . . vigorous, glowing experience that stimulates all with whom we come in contact. The peace of the Christian depends not upon peaceful conditions in the world about him but upon the indwelling of the Spirit of God."[14]

As the poet Power said:

Trust in yourself, and you are doomed to disappointment.

Trust in your friends, and they will die and leave you.

Trust in money, and you may have it taken from you.

Trust in reputation, and some slanderous tongue may blast it.

But—trust in God, and you are never to be confounded in time or eternity.

But what about when I just don't believe in God? Not from contrariness, but that I simply don't have the belief that there is a God?

Even here, there is a promise. The Bible says we should:

Taste and see that the Lord is good;

Seek and we will find;

Knock and the door will be opened.

It's understandable that not all are believers, but even an unbeliever can

81

give God the test.

The Bible says to seek God with all your heart. This means giving God an honest, open chance to show you that He cares. After all, the most important discovery of your life could be that God is real!

---

[1] J. S. Levin, H. Y. Vanderpool, "Is frequent religious attendance really conducive to better health? Toward an epidemiology of religion," *Social Science and Medicine,* 1987; 24(7): pp. 589-600.

[2] J. D. Kark, et al., *American Journal of Public Health,* 1996: 86(3); pp. 341-346.

[3] J. S. Levin, L. M. Chatters, R. J. Taylor, "Religious effects on health status and life satisfaction among black Americans," *Journals of Gerontology Series B: Psychological Sciences and Social Sciences,* May 1995; 50(3): pp. S154-163.

[4] C. G. Ellison, "Race, Religious Involvement, and Depressive Symptomatology in a Southeastern US Community," *Social Science and Medicine,* 1995:40 (11); pp. 1561-1572.

[5] V. J. Shoenback, et al., "Social Ties and Mortality in Evans County GA," *American Journal of Epidemiology,* 1986; 123: pp. 577-591.

[6] C. G. Ellison, "Religious involvement and subjective well-being," *Journal of Health and Social Behavior,* Mar. 1991; 32(1): pp. 80-99.

[7] J. W. Dwyer, L. L. Clarke, M. K. Miller, "The effect of religious concentration and affiliation on county cancer mortality rates," *Journal of Health and Social Behavior,* June 1990; 31(2): pp. 185-202.

[8] H. G. Koenig, *The Power of Healing Faith,* p. 72, 1999, quoting P. H. Hardestyn and K. M. Kirby, "Relation Between Family Religious and Drug Use Within Adolescent Peer Groups," *Journal of Social Behavior and Personality,* 10:(1) 1995.

[9] A. Y. Amoateng, S. J. Bahr, "Religion, Family, and Adolescent Drug Use," *Social Perspectives,* 29: (1) 1986; pp. 53-76.

[10] *The Healing Power of Faith* (Simon & Schuster, April, 1999), p. 177.

[11] J. Marks, "A Time Out," *U.S. News & World Report,* Dec. 11, 1995: pp. 85-97.

[12] *Journal of Psychology & Theology,* 1991; 19(1): pp. 71-83.

[13] L. Dossey, *Healing Words: The Power of Prayer and the Practice of Medicine* (New York: HarperCollins Publisher, 1993), p. 18.

[14] *SDA Bible Commentary,* vol. 4, p. 203.

CHAPTER 7

RESTORING RESILIENCY

Close now thine eyes and rest secure;
Thy soul is safe enough, thy body sure;
He that loves thee, He that keeps
And guards thee, never slumbers, never sleeps.
— *"A Good Night," Francis Quarles*

R Is for Rest—the Restorer of Our Resiliency

I really enjoy GoogleEarth. One can explore ocean beds, mountain ranges, and even use it as a time machine. I guess it's my imagination that transforms it into a time machine for me.

Last week I awoke early, then drifted into that twilight zone of snoozing. The scientific name for that semiconscious awakening phase is a hypnopompic state. I became nostalgic as my thoughts drifted back to childhood and I relived some of the times I spent with my now deceased parents. It's strange how we can relive events, sometimes so vividly, when in the interphase between asleep and awake.

Though I believe I have processed my grief over the loss of my parents, I still feel their legacy of blessing and perhaps I appreciate them more now than I did when they were alive. When I awoke fully I decided to let my wife sleep on and went to the computer. There I pulled up GoogleEarth and found the town where I'd lived some 55 years ago. What a way to go back to the England of my childhood!

To my surprise, I found our actual street. Then, traipsing around the old neighborhood, I found my old grammar school. At least it looked like my school, as far as its location. Obviously, they had built a bigger swimming pool, and more buildings, but the playing fields were there. The name of the school popped up, and it was different—but then, a sidebar flashed on, and I saw that the history of the school included the name of it when I attended so many years ago.

I traced the roads I ran on as a child, and found I'd run quite long distances, though I need to get my youngest son to show me how to measure distances on these Google maps. I found the Coldfall Woods I'd played in for hours, and discovered that its claim to fame is that glaciation of the United Kingdom was first proved there. How they did that, I didn't explore. In fact, I remembered the woods only for the giant oaks, the hazelnut trees, and the streams where a group of us kids spent hours building little dams. My mind went to the hours we spent climbing trees and knocking down horse chestnuts, with which we played "conkers." Then, to my amazement, I found the "allotments" or gardens that people could rent —obviously still sources of pleasure and recreation. As children, we'd watch whom we thought were old men sitting in their deck chairs, sunning themselves after a couple of hours tending their vegetable plots. I remembered, then found, the street where we gangs of kids played marbles and raced our Dinky cars. I remembered the time we strung a length of string between two lampposts, and fired our "solid-fuel jet-ex powered rockets" along the thread. Life seemed so carefree, the street a natural place to play, the woods a refuge, and even though the demands at school were strenuous we always had time to play.

Then I thought of my grandchildren with their lives full of lessons. One is learning to play the harp and the clarinet, her sister the viola and the drums, the youngest the piano and the flute. My grandsons play the piano and take singing lessons, art lessons, tennis lessons, and karate. When I was a kid playing down the street or in the woods, my parents would come to the front gate and shout or whistle, signaling me it was time to come home. That could never happen with my grandkids, for they're never out on the street. It's too dangerous! There are "predators" out there!

My daughter does worry about mountain lions where they live in a rural part of town. But it's human predators my son is worried about with his three girls.

Recently my wife and I discussed whether society really is more dangerous—or could it be that when we kids were out playing together we kept each other safer. I don't know, but it seems we had a lot more recreation—just good strengthening exercise—when I was a boy than kids have now. I doubt my grandchildren get to climb trees, make go-carts, use a catapult, make bows and arrows, ride their bikes for miles, rob birds' nests, play hare and hounds in creeks and woods, have secret societies, or build their own tree forts—from which they might possibly fall. All of that is too dangerous.

Instead, a variety of lessons to enrich their lives. They work on computers, play games that teach them their times tables, and learn to be afraid of strangers. Along the way they're getting ready for adulthood as fast as we can get them there. They need to have "*done*" a lot of things to get into law school or medical school or even the university they've chosen. It doesn't look too good on a resumé that they frittered away their childhood in play.

Life is pretty hectic for today's kids and I wonder what the long-term effect will be. It wasn't until I almost drowned in my university workload that I realized life was strenuous. My first job kept me on call 24 hours a day, six days a week. As a medical resident—what in the U.S. they call an intern— I *lived* in the hospital, making me a true resident. Only a half day off per week, up and down all night long, I became a walking zombie. I remember that once I was so exhausted that I awoke outside my room, wondering who it was that had called me. It slowly dawned on me that I had dreamed I was called and had gotten up in a state of complete exhaustion.

Where is the balance in life? How do we strike the right balance between work and play? It is, perhaps, one of the hardest lessons we have to learn. I trained in two specialties, first in pediatrics, then obstetrics and gynecology. Looking back, I realize that the programs were designed to extract all the energy we possibly could muster. On call every second night and working every day meant that we had a mere 10 hours out of every 48 for sleep, family, or anything else. Four years of this made one a workaholic who felt guilty for taking a day off for self or family. Medical practice was ever-demanding. Day and night our lives were ruled by women in labor and one emergency after another. Exhausted, we would retreat to a nearby cottage for rest and recuperation. A little more balance would have been more appropriate. There is no space to praise, much less to be "living praise" when work is all-consuming.

The interesting thing is that we actually achieve more when living a balanced life. When I was a student some of my friends would sit for three-hour stretches with their head in the books. Long before I heard the term "attention span," I knew an hour was enough for me. I'd read for an hour, then get up and walk. If I could get a friend to accompany me, all the better. We could discuss what we'd read and after about 15 minutes could go back to tackle another subject. The surprise was that I'd remember so much more than some of those marathon studiers!

Jesus understood the need for rest and restoration. The people clamored—people always clamor—for more. After a time, He would withdraw from the crowd, giving both Himself and His disciples some space apart, a little time for refreshment. Jesus was relaxed enough to sleep through a storm, and free enough to ignore the man-made rules of the Pharisees. When they complained that His disciples worked on Sabbath because they rubbed a few grains of wheat in their hands to get off the husks, He rebuked them for their narrow-mindedness. On another occasion, Jesus accused them of making such obsessive rules that they became a hindrance to the blessing of Sabbath rest. Jesus declared that He was Lord of the Sabbath, that the Sabbath was not another burden, but a blessing. This holy time, this 24 hours, had been made for people. People were not made for the Sabbath. Jesus recognized the tyranny of work and the necessity of a time set apart for rest.

Individuals need rest and recreation, but families need it too. Nothing builds the strength of a family as recreation enjoyed together. True health involves every aspect of our lives. It's more than healthy organs and tissues. Good mental health is also essential to our well-being. Social interaction with family and friends is the principle safeguard for our children. To be able to play together, sing together, rest head-in-lap with each other, just hang out together—all these build the bonds of a healthy social life.

Social and behavioral scientists have discovered that when it comes to building resiliency in our young people, the most important thing is a relationship with a balanced, caring, wholesome adult. Such bonds and relationships are forged in time spent together.

Completing the work of creation, even God paused. As He looked at a cosmos set in motion, and the web of interdependent life, God saw that the next essential was rest. In giving a day of rest, a cycle of evening and morning and a pattern of sleep and activity, God set apart time for us to renew.

We all require rest. We've all felt the weight of weariness. We all know the symptoms of fatigue, the aching neck, the fuzzy head, and muscle pain, that deep heaviness that accompanies exhaustion. Not only do we have physical symptoms, we become aware of mental stress. We feel the tension in the muscles at the back of our neck, but we don't feel the tension in the muscles of our arteries. With building tension may come rising blood pressure or a migraine. Our whole being screams for rest.

Jesus was able to say, "Come to me, all you who are weary and burdened, and I will give you rest. Take my yoke upon you and learn from me" (Matt. 11:28, 29, NIV).

The "yoke" referred to here may well have been the yoke or shawl of the rabbi. Learn my ways, Jesus seems to be saying. The Scriptures tell us, "Be still, and know that I am God" (Ps. 46:10). That may be the best advice in the world. Stop the hubbub, the rushing, the frenzy. *Be still.*

EVEN A PROPHET MUST REST

For more than three years drought had parched the land of Samaria. King Ahab and his wife Jezebel felt the political pressure of a starving people, and then that gadfly, the prophet Elijah, called them to a showdown. Priests of Baal and thousands of people gathered there by Mount Carmel.

They were desperate for water, and so was the land. After three years with no rain all streams were dry and most of the vegetation gone. So Elijah challenged them to ask their gods to intervene. He would ask the Lord.

The priests of Baal began their incantations, their dancing, their sexual gyrating, building into a frenzy of shouting, rhythm, and sound, but Baal was silent. No fire fell from the sky to consume their sacrifice. Elijah urged them on. "Perhaps your god is sleeping. Perhaps he's on a journey," he said. Hours passed. Noon came and went and still the sun burned in the sky. The day rushed toward evening. At last, in exhaustion, the priests of Baal gave up. Their god had not answered.

Then Elijah rebuilt the altar of God. Precious water was brought at his command, and the altar was soaked, the trench around it filled. Everyone watched as Elijah lifted his arms heavenward and prayed. In that instant— a miracle. From the clear blue sky, a blaze of fire shot down onto the altar, consuming the sacrifice—the Creator God demonstrating His reality to the idol worshippers.

After this display, Elijah prophesied that rain would come, and a small cloud, the size of a man's hand, appeared in the west. Then with superhuman strength, Elijah ran ahead of King Ahab's chariot to the gates of Jezreel, but after all the excitement he was exhausted. Soaked to the skin, terrified of Queen Jezebel, he fled a full day's journey, then collapsed and slept. God let him sleep, then sent an angel to awaken him and give him something to eat.

Elijah, still tired beyond endurance, begged God to let him die. Instead, God, who knows the limits of His servants, gave him strength—and a few final jobs to do. Then in an act of extreme grace and appreciation, God sent a heavenly taxi to carry Elijah to his rest.

God made our bodies to benefit from many different kinds of rest. Rest is absolutely essential to health, and we deny our bodies of it to our detriment. Let's explore the physiology of rest. When we understand it, we'll be able to get the most benefit from it.

REST FOR THE WEARY

Today's society is full of fatigued individuals, fighting, pushing, and striving to keep up in the human "race." Over time, cheating our bodies out of sleep can produce serious physical and emotional loss. In the U.S. fatigue ranks among the 10 most common reasons for visiting a physician.[1] In fact, each year 3.3 million Americans visit their doctors for insomnia.[2] It is estimated that as many as 60 percent of Americans have some problems relating to their sleep, similar to those around the world.[3, 4]

We need rest, for rest provides time for the body to restore that which it has used. There are two types of rest:

- Daily rest

- Periodic rest

In one day the average heart beats 110,000 times, and the blood runs through millions of miles of arteries, veins, and capillaries. We speak thousands of words, breathe 28,000 times, move major muscles hundreds of times, and operate some 15-20 billion brain cells. No wonder sleep is important in restoring our energy and maintaining health. As Shakespeare wrote: "Sleep . . . wraps up the raveled sleeve of care."

A newborn baby sleeps an average of 20 hours a day; a 6-year-old, 10 hours; a 12-year-old, nine hours; and an adult, approximately eight hours. Whether these averages are optimal varies according to the individual. Breslow and Belloc, in their famous Alameda County study, showed that people who sleep eight to nine hours a night seemed to have better health outcomes than those who sleep less or longer periods of time. Rarely we find some people—such as Ben Franklin and Thomas Edison—who can get by with four or five hours of sleep a night, but these are exceptions, not the rule. Many who sleep fewer hours at night take short catnaps throughout the day. Albert Einstein required at least nine hours of sleep. Adequate sleep should remove sleepiness and drowsiness during the day and permit a sense of well-being and alertness.

Students who study all night prior to an exam often suffer the consequences of sleep deprivation—inferior grades. Work schedules that don't permit adequate sleep can result in increased inattention in the workplace.

The physiology of sleep is incompletely understood. Current theories suggest that sleep is an active inhibition of some of the brain functions from a level in the brainstem below the midpons.[5]

Sleep corrects two major physiological effects. The first is on the nervous system itself, where prolonged wakefulness is associated with a serious progressive malfunction in thought processes as well as emotional balance. The second effect on the body is not as clear but is mediated by the sympathetic nervous system.

The area in the brainstem thought to cause sleep is the raphe nuclei in the lower half of the pons. Extensions proceed from these nuclei to most of the limbic system of the brain, the thalamus, as well as the hypothalamus and reticular system, and in their terminal ending they release serotonin. Agents inhibiting serotonin formation are associated with an inability to sleep.

Because of this finding, serotonin has been assumed to play a role in promoting sleep. Other neurotransmitters may also play a role in sleep.

Studies performed in sleep laboratories, using electroencephalographs, which record the electrical activity of the brain, have demonstrated two major types of sleep activity. The electroencephalograph reflects the electrical waves indicative of brain activity during sleep.

* **Nonrapid eye movement (NREM) sleep.** This state of physical rest has three stages:

Stage 1: Brain activity is similar to that of a person who is awake. One feels drowsy but is still aware of noises and sounds.

Stage 2: Brain waves are slower and larger and one becomes more relaxed. Arousal is more difficult.

Stage 3: Brain waves become large and slow, known as delta waves. This is a deep state of relaxation, in which the sleeper is oblivious to what is going on. This is sound sleep.

* **Rapideye movement (REM) sleep** is important for the restoration of mental and emotional functions. It is known as mental rest. During REM sleep, the electroencephalographic record will suddenly show a burst of electrical activity similar to that of a person who is awake. The eyes move back and forth rapidly. During this phase individuals may snore, sleepwalk, wet the bed, grind teeth, and/or dream, even though recall of dream content may be less than clear.

The entire cycle takes about 90 minutes and may be repeated from four to six times a night. Both the NREM and REM sleep are important in order to ensure complete physical and mental rest.[6]

The body works on a daily 24-hour cycle. This is based on the natural seasonal variations in the length of the day and night. Generally the length of daylight influences the timing of the release of hormones and the intensity of their secretion.

Hormones whose secretion is influenced by sleep patterns include:

Cortisol. This hormone is secreted during sleep in the second half of the sleep period, preparing the body for the next day's activities. Cortisol has numerous effects: influencing blood glucose levels, regulating sodium and potassium concentrations, regulating blood pressure, and influencing muscle strength. Regular sleep habits result in regular patterns of cortisol secretion.

Growth hormone. This hormone is secreted at its maximal rate during sleep. It has an effect on glucose and amino acid metabolism.

Melatonin. Secretion rates increase during the night but may have more of a role to play in sleep regulation.

A number of factors influence sleep. These include:

Irregular sleep schedule. Going to bed and getting up at odd times, working different shifts, travel across time zones, and weekend changes in sleep fight against good sleep patterns.

A quiet bedroom, free of bright light and noise, properly ventilated, and a comfortable temperature will aid in sleeping.

The time preceding retiring should be free of arguments, exciting TV, and stressful events. It should be a quiet time to wind down the day's activity.

Regular exercise and avoiding excessive fatigue aids good sleep.

The last meal of the day should be light and taken a few hours prior to retiring.

A warm, not hot, bath may help relaxation before going to bed.

Avoid alcohol, tobacco, caffeine, and other chemical substances that interfere with the normal sleep patterns.

Medical conditions such as sleep apnea, respiratory disorders, cardiac conditions, phobias, and other psychiatric disorders may require professional assistance.

The Bible recommends a weekly rest, and such a rest seems to provide a much needed break from the tedium of work. In fact, periodic rest provides many benefits. During World War II productivity increased about 15 percent when the nonstop work schedule was reduced to a 48-hour work-week. This demonstrated that even under the pressures of war there are limits on how long people can work and remain productive.[lii]

On July 29, 1941, six months before the United States entered the war, Prime Minister Winston Churchill announced in the House of Commons, "If we are to win this war it will be by staying power. For this reason we must have one holiday per week and one week holiday per year." This was voted into law.

Periodic rest should include annual vacations. These vacations are not necessarily periods of idleness, but events and activities outside the usual routine. Such vacations provide mental and emotional renewal, increase creativity, and bond family relationships.

The Lord our Creator knows that our bodies need a balanced daily rest—physically, mentally, emotionally, and socially. He also knows that to function at our best we also need a weekly rest, as stated in Exodus 20:8-10: "Remember the Sabbath day, to keep it holy. Six days you shall labor and do all your work, but the seventh day is the Sabbath of the Lord your

God. In it you shall do no work: you, nor your son, nor your daughter, nor your manservant, nor your maidservant, nor your cattle, nor your stranger who is within your gates."

The Lord wants us, His children, to have fellowship with Him especially on the Sabbath day. Part of the blessing of Sabbath rest comes as we support and relate with each other. The Sabbath was made for us; we were not made for the Sabbath (see Mark 2:27). Regular sleep and weekly rest empowers us to be receptive to the blessing of God so He can fill our living with praise.

Of all the types of rest, none is so meaningful as the rest from sinning. Many years ago God took a long look at His chosen people and told them their sacrifices to Him were an abomination and their fasting and rituals a farce, because they had not rested from their sinful ways. He did not want their fasts or sacrifices, as they were meaningless. God told them, "Is this not the fast that I have chosen: to loose the bonds of wickedness, to undo the heavy burdens, to let the oppressed go free, and that you break every yoke? Is it not to share your bread with the hungry, and that you bring to your house the poor who are cast out; when you see the naked, that you cover him, and not hide yourself from your own flesh?" (Isa. 58:6, 7).

While rest is good, and "all work and no play makes Jack a dull boy," it is the balance between work and play, action and rest that yields the greatest reward.

"Some make themselves sick by overwork. For these, rest, freedom from care, and a spare diet, are essential to restoration of health. To those who are brain weary and nervous because of continual labor and close confinement, a visit to the country, where they can live a simple, carefree life, coming in close contact with the things of nature, will be most helpful. Roaming through the fields and the woods, picking the flowers, listening to the songs of the birds, will do far more than any other agency toward their recovery" (*Ministry of Healing*, pp. 236, 237).

"Our Redeemer is constantly working to restore in [us] the moral image of God. And although the whole creation groans under the curse, and fruit and flowers are nothing in comparison with what they will be in the earth made new, yet even today the sick may find health and gladness and joy in field and orchard. What a restorative this is!" (17MR, 354.2).

"The Sabbath and the family were alike instituted in Eden, and in God's purpose they are indissolubly linked together. On this day more than on any other, it is possible for us to live the life of Eden. It was God's plan for the members of the family to be associated in work and study, in worship and recreation, the father as priest of his household, and both father and mother as teachers and companions of their children. But the results of sin, having changed the conditions of life, to a great degree prevent this association. Often the father hardly sees the faces of his children throughout the week. He is almost wholly deprived of opportunity for companionship or instruction. But God's love has set a limit to the demands of toil. Over the Sabbath He places His merciful hand. In His own day He preserves for the family opportunity for communion with Him, with nature, and with one another" (*Child Guidance*, pp. 535, 536).

"The Sabbath should be made so interesting to our families that its weekly return will be hailed with joy. In no better way can parents exalt and honor the Sabbath than by devising means to impart proper instruction to their families and interesting them in spiritual things, giving them correct views of the character of God and what He requires of us in order to perfect Christian characters and attain to eternal life. Parents, make the Sabbath a delight, that your children may look forward to it and have a welcome in their hearts for it" (*Child Guidance*, p. 536).

---

[1]E. Nelson, J. Kirk, et al., "Chief complaint fatigue: a longitudinal study from the patient's perspective," *Family Practice Research Journal,* 1987 Summer 6(4): pp. 175-188.

[2]S. E. Radecki, S. A. Brunton, "Management of insomnia in office-based practice. National prevalence and therapeutic patterns," *Archives of Family Medicine,* Nov. 1993; 2(11): pp. 1129-1134.

[3]D. J. Foly, A. A. Monjan, et al., "Sleep complaints among elderly persons: an epidemiologic study of three communities," *Sleep* July 1995; 18(6): pp. 425-432.

[4]S. Coren, "The prevalence of self-reported sleep disturbances in young adults," *International Journal of Neuroscience,* Nov. 1994; 79 (1-2): pp. 67-73.

[5]A. C. Guyton, J. E. Hall, *Textbook of Medical Physiology* (Philadelphia: W. B. Saunders, 2000), p. 690.

[6]*Ibid.,* p. 689.

[7]R. R. Sayers, "Major studies of fatigue," *War Medicine* 2:786, 1942.

CHAPTER 8

AN ATMOSPHERE OF PRAISE

From the cool cisterns of the midnight air
My spirit drank repose;
The fountain of perpetual peace flows there—
From those deep cisterns flows.
— *"Hymn to the Night," Henry Wadsworth Longfellow*

A Is for Air—the Activator of Our Vitality

Several still-to-do activities of high priority remain on my radar, and one of them is to take a tour of the Holy Land. I feel certain that my understanding of so much of the Bible would be enlightened and put into a crystalline focus if I could see the actual places one reads about. Nevertheless, sometimes the images our minds create are just as vivid and possibly as meaningful for us as if we were actually there ourselves.

I'm not sure that the upper room used by the disciples was the same one used by Jesus for the Last Supper, but I suppose it could have been. I imagine the meaning Christ's presence would have given to the room. His breaking of bread and then the offering of the cup, and His immortal words: "Take, eat; this is My body." "This is My blood of the new covenant, which is shed for many." The room where Jesus appeared to His disciples and other friends after His resurrection, where He ate fish and honeycomb to prove that He was alive and real. The room where He appeared for Thomas, taking the doubter's hand, willing to have Thomas explore the scars with his fingers. I'm sure this room was a sacred place for the disciples.

Jesus told them that they should stay in Jerusalem until they were given the Comforter. Daily gathering together, I'm sure they told and retold stories from their years with Jesus. They must have relived their memories of His miracles and sermons, and simply the talks they had together. Then, in prayer, they would seek the will of God for their lives. I can imagine this as a time of anxiety and even fear as they struggled for a sense of purpose and meaning. They had seen Jesus ascend into the heavens. Afterward they'd stood open-mouthed, gazing into the blue sky. The angel had said Jesus would come again, but when? And what was their role to be as they waited?

At a loss, they were at prayer and praise when something happened that they could not have imagined. The door was locked. Some were seated, some stood; perhaps some were talking in groups. Suddenly the sound of rushing wind filled the room and flames of fire flickered over each head. I can imagine them gasping, looking around, trying to comprehend what was happening. Then in the same way that Elijah had felt the wind, seen the fire, and then through a still, small voice became aware of the presence of God, the disciples felt the Holy Spirit take them into captivity. A transformation seeps through their every conscious thought, and each knows he has been pervasively changed. Every particle of their being comes into the orbit of the Spirit.

This analogy of the Spirit coming as the wind or air had been used by Moses as he wrote of Adam's awakening to life. The words used are "and God breathed" into his nostrils the breath of life.

We can better understand the aptness of this metaphor when we understand the role of oxygen as an essence of life. Essential for the metabolism of every molecule of carbohydrate, protein, or fat on earth—oxygen is the essential facilitator. Without oxygen, all life on earth would cease. Without the presence of oxygen in every mitochondria, life would come to a grinding halt!

Air is a mixture of gases: 78 percent nitrogen, 21 percent oxygen, and 0.9 percent argon; the rest are other gases such as carbon dioxide, helium, hydrogen, etc. At any given time you carry approximately two quarts of oxygen in your blood, lungs, and body tissues. Brain cells deprived of oxygen for more than four minutes begin to die. For this reason the American Lung Association's motto, "It's a matter of life and breath," is very accurate. The ability to breathe, as well as an understanding of the importance of the vital element oxygen, is essential. We need air for life and good fresh air for health.

Oxygen provides efficient cell function by permitting the metabolism of nutrients and the transfer of energy within cells. That's why we need to breathe pure, clean fresh air. Fresh air in buildings is destroyed when tobacco smoke, city smog, and other pollutants are recirculated through the air conditioning systems. On the other hand, good quality clean air usually abounds in natural outdoor environments, especially around evergreen trees, green plants in mountains and forests, near moving waters such as lakes, oceans, rivers, and waterfalls, and after rain. It is estimated that the ocean's algae provides almost 90 percent of the oxygen in our atmosphere, with the other 10 percent coming from land plants. Fresh air is invigorating! Notice how exhilarated you feel near a waterfall or at the ocean. This may be one reason for the popularity of resorts and vacation areas in the mountains and by the sea.

In homes and offices live plants encourage fresh air, removing carbon dioxide and freshening the air with oxygen.

Polluted air is found on freeways, at airports, and in closed, poorly ventilated areas. Polluted, smoke-filled air can be associated with increased anxiety, migraine headaches, nausea, vomiting, eye problems, irritability, and respiratory congestion. Six million people, mostly children, die each year from acute respiratory infections that are complicated by indoor pollution usually originating from unvented or poorly vented cooking facilities. Worldwide acute respiratory infection deaths are three times that of malaria and of greater importance than diarrhea. Because fresh air is important to your health, you should make an effort to breathe natural clean air, for example, during outdoor morning exercise. Your whole body will be energized far beyond anything you might achieve exercising in stale, recirculated air or that found in smoky rooms, congested offices, or noisy factories.

So many reports of discomfort and specific symptoms are related to office environments that a term has been coined to describe it: sick-building syndrome. This is particularly noted in sealed buildings with centrally controlled, mechanical ventilation. Associated conditions include allergies, infections, Legionnaire's disease, and worsening of asthma because of airborne irritants. This highlights the importance of breathing fresh, clean air.

Breathing is a natural spontaneous automatic activity. We take in and move out approximately 20,000 liters of air every day. As the air is inhaled by our lungs, the exchange of oxygen and carbon dioxide takes place in more than 600 million air sacs called alveoli. The alveoli are lined by a network of fine capillaries containing blood.

Air and blood are separated by these thin walls, only two cells thick. Here the exchange of gases by diffusion occurs. Blood that is low in oxygen, but full of carbon dioxide, is brought to the lungs so that the carbon dioxide may be released and oxygen picked up. Then many millions of red blood cells carry the oxygen-rich blood to all the body's cells and tissues, nourishing them, giving them life. This exchange of oxygen and carbon dioxide occurs in milliseconds, and it takes only about one minute for a complete circuit of the body!

Nanotechnology has permitted ultramicroscopic imaging of the flow of oxygen. I recall seeing video imagery of the flow of oxygen through a mitochondrion, as though it were a stream of water rushing through the interior of the energy powerhouse of a cell. Such molecules of oxygen, essential to life, are like God's Spirit or power in the life.

Of course, an atheist does not see these parallels, but to a believer, God's Spirit is as essential and pervasive as oxygen.

The process of death does not lend itself to fine biochemical study. However, there is a process to dying. I have watched people die, and the helplessness of the physician in the presence of the terminally ill is an experience I abhor. Nonetheless, it is real. Metabolic products gradually accumulate, cellular mechanisms that normally regulate intra- and extracellular concentrations of electrolytes fall behind in their efforts at balance. The body's utilization of oxygen becomes inefficient; failing circulation falls behind in its distribution. Centers in the medulla begin to stimulate deeper breathing. The person may gasp for breath, but partial pressures of oxygen continue to fall. As the dying process continues, physicians may infuse fluids and correct acid balance, but unless the process can be reversed, the patient loses consciousness. Oxygen no longer replaces carbon dioxide, blackness engulfs, and a final gasping breath indicates a cellular closing down that epitomizes dying.

Just as oxygen and air are essential, so is God's Spirit as the enlivening agent of our life.

VACATIONS

Vacations are so precious to families. Our family has enjoyed many vacations together and one of our favorite places is the islands of the Turks and Caicos in the Caribbean. Once while vacationing there, my wife and I decided to learn to scuba dive. The classes were very interesting. First, we learned how the scuba apparatus works. The regulator is an essential piece of the equipment, permitting the diver to suck in air from the tank without getting the air at the pressure it is in the tank. Air is compressed in the tank, up to perhaps 3,000 pounds per square inch. However, the regulator allows the air to be present in the mask at the ambient pressure, and the sucking of this air opens a valve to permit more to flow from the tank.

The interesting thing is that as one goes beneath the water, the pressure increases with the depth. At 32 feet the pressure increases by the same amount as the pressure of one atmosphere—or roughly 14 pounds per square inch. This means that the volume of a bucket of air on the surface is half a bucket volume at a depth of 32 feet. Each additional 32 feet of depth further compresses the air in the regulator, meaning the concentration or density of the air being breathed is increased. Because a diver themself is compressed and the pressure is distributed evenly through the body, the increased pressure does not result in circulatory changes of great magnitude at depths up to 100 feet.

Time becomes a factor, however, because as the gases diffuse into tissues, they do so at this increased pressure. Divers notice a marked change in the volume of air in their ears as they descend the first 15 to 30 feet, where the volume will shrink 50 percent. Changes become of an ever-decreasing magnitude as one dives the next 30 feet, and slow descent may cause minimal discomfort after the initial 30 or so feet. Of course, on the ascent, the expansion of gases occurs.

I remember when I first began diving, at about 40 feet I was having trouble with my buoyancy control. I inflated my vest with too much air, and began floating upward. The air in my vest expanded rapidly as I floated up, making my ascent faster. Panicking a little, I tried to empty the vest (called a buoyancy control device, BCD), but pressed the "intake" rather than the "deflate" button.

At that, I started shooting toward the surface. Realizing that such a rapid ascent was very dangerous I began to "shout" out the air in my lungs. My continuous exhalation was accompanied by thoughts of the bends. This is where the air in the tissues, suddenly released from pressure, forms bubbles. If this happens in small blood vessels, it can plug them and should such vessels be in the brain, serious damage would occur. Fortunately, I'd managed to dive just some 40 feet and had been down only a few minutes—so I'm here to write about the event. Had I been down, say 80 feet for 30 or 40 minutes I might have been in serious difficulty.

Every cell in our bodies receives oxygen and even the inert nitrogen in the air we breathe. This means that heart, brain, kidneys, lungs, bones, liver, muscle, skin all get air, but in particular—oxygen.

OUR WHOLE LIFE

In a special way, the breath of God or His Spirit influences every aspect of our lives. It is this involvement with every fiber of our being that is at the heart of the belief held by Seventh-day Adventists that health care involves every aspect of an individual's well-being. In our healthcare institutions, we speak of "whole person" care. In fact, the motto of the General Conference healthcare institution, Loma Linda Medical Center, is "To make man whole." The "man" is, of course, generic—meaning mankind—but the "whole" may not be as completely understood.

God is concerned with the whole. John expressed a like concern when he wrote to Gaius, "I pray that you may prosper in all things and be in health, just as your soul prospers."

The breath of God, or His Spirit, is concerned for the "whole" of us.

Some will focus on the physical understanding, for example, that the complexity of a metabolic derangement such as diabetes requires a knowledge of anatomy and physiology. Endocrinologists specialize in such knowledge, and the interplay between diet and metabolism is well understood by them. The role of exercise in regulating blood sugar is also well recognized. Often an understanding of the resistance to insulin seen in type II diabetes covers a wide range of biochemisty. Nutritional factors, such as the role different proteins may play on insulin resistance, will be weighed in conjunction with an understanding of the role of different fatty acids. So it is easy to become immersed in the complexity, so enthralled by the finesse of metabolic processes, that sight is lost of the *"whole."*

Sometimes they forget the "whole" patient. They may be totally involved in weighing the effects of medication on insulin secretion or sensitivity, and so concerned over the meticulous management of the patient's blood sugar, that their bedside manner becomes brusque and sharp. Or thinking of the studies that show enormous benefits of one group of medicines over another, the physician may be prescriptive and authoritarian—then be surprised when their patient changes doctors, perhaps to one less skilled or knowledgeable.

But intuitively the patient knows something is missing. They feel as though they're on a production line. Their doctor was not treating their whole.

The Holy Spirit affects not just our physical selves, but the whole. Should we wish to take care of ourselves, we too need to be like the Holy Spirit, and address every component of our whole life. Diet and exercise, sleep, rest, and sunshine may improve our physical being, but they also involve our mental parts.

Mental health is as important as physical health. Recently I was at an airport looking for a book to read on the plane, when I saw a book titled *I Hope They Serve Beer in Hell*. Interested as I am in the balance of life or "temperance" as religious people know it, I picked up the book to see if it would be helpful to me. It soon became apparent that it was a candid portrayal of a sordid life. The writer spoke of binge drinking, sexual promiscuity, and an apparently endless round of hedonistic forays as an expression of his individuality and freedom. On the book cover were excerpts of comments labeling the author as "vile," "emancipated," a "demon," or an "icon"—depending on the mindset of the reader. Obviously, the mental attitude of both the author and his readers will impact their health in very tangible ways, a little down the pathway of time.

In her wonderful book *Mindset* Carol Dweck shows how important our mind-set is to our enjoyment and success in life. It is also important to our health, our ability to praise, and indeed to be living praise.

This is why we are admonished, "Let this mind be in you which was also in Christ Jesus." Indeed, the fruit of the Spirit manifests itself in mental attributes of love, joy, peace, patience, gentleness, and meekness.

As the molecules of oxygen stream into the organelles of every cell, so the "breath" of life—the Holy Spirit—infuses the mind with thoughts that are pure, good, lovely, and loving.

It is difficult for someone in pain to have balanced thinking, and vice versa. People with unbalanced thoughts have difficulty in maintaining good physical health. But beyond our physical health is our emotional health.

Children were often given IQ tests when I was a boy. These tests later were shown to be biased by culture, social standing, and many other factors. Additionally, teachers hearing a student had a higher or lower IQ treated them that way, with results in learning that were shown to become self-fulfilling prophecies. More recently, we have learned of "emotional intelligence" —the EIQ. Such numbers are extremely limited in their application, but do illustrate that certain factors impact our health more than just our physical well-being.

We have all read of the long-term trauma inflicted upon those who were emotionally abused as children. We sometimes are oblivious to the impact our behaviors can have on others. This is especially true of the health of our family members. A repetitive demeaning of a partner, perhaps in word, deed, or action leads to emotional ill health. Failing to give credit and affirmation, being quick to be sarcastic or to mention someone's mistakes, may arise from our own emotional ill health and insecurity. Parents who drive their children, as I had a tendency to do, may be insecure and want to protect them from insecurity, but—in reality—teaches them to be insecure. Failure to reach parental expectations can cause major distress.

Depression among adolescents is on the rise, and may reflect increasing expectations and increasing isolation.

The son of one of my patients was expected to get a grade point average of 4.0 (i.e. 100 percent all the time). When a test he took came back in the 90s, he attempted suicide by breathing the exhaust fumes of his car. He soon became hypoxic, but was found before he died—only to have to live with his brain damage.

The "breath of God" brings *joy* as one of its fruits, and the desire of God brought through His Spirit is perhaps in no way more powerful than this desire that we experience joy. Another way the Spirit imparts our "living praise" is that He brings hope. As I grow older, I realize more and more the finiteness of our lives. As more friends become victims of disease, degenerative processes, and death, hope becomes a dearly cherished emotion. Hope is needed in situations where cancer is marauding or where Alzheimer's darkly clouds the lives of a family. Hope becomes an emotion of survival, and the Spirit assures the emotional part of our being with the promise of salvation.

While hope may be more cherished as we get older, among the young their social health depends even more powerfully on relationships. We are physical, mental, emotional, and social beings. Our social health is also influenced by the work of the Spirit, as it saturates even this aspect of our lives.

A society that accepts the values given by a faith in God is prodded toward tolerance, compassion, protection of the weak, and nurture of the vulnerable. It becomes a gentler, kinder society. Young people who feel the influence of the Spirit become more accepting, inclusive, and tolerant of physical, mental, and emotional imperfections. All benefit from such relationships. Sadly, the loss of spiritual and moral education in our schools will lead to generations of faithless, morally bankrupt people.

The most powerful, cohesive force in gang dynamics is the acceptance that being a gang member confers. The bonds between gang members become a powerful means of transmitting gang values. Violence—robbing, beating, even rape and murder—become accepted values, adopted because of the emotional need to be accepted by the group. Again and again it has been shown that secure, supportive, loyal relationships are the single most important conduits of the sharing of values.

Similarly, service is the practical outworking that entrenches values into the lives of teens and young adults. So often, education is given as a stream of facts, a didactic set of lessons, and we wonder what went wrong. Why don't 85 percent of teens use condoms for at-risk sex, when 99 percent of them know the risk they're taking? "How is it," we ask, "that kids who know smoking is harmful, take up the habit anyway?"

Clearly, the answer is that the social and emotional pressures are greater than the mental assent to the facts. So pernicious can be the results of these at-risk behaviors that the young man or woman succumbs to conditions that produce lifetime problems. Youth infected by HIV live a life of anxiety, remorse, and the endless battling of disease. The tobacco addict may, like Mark Twain, quit dozens of times, only to repeatedly fall victim to the siren calls of Lady Nicotine. Even President Barack Obama, for all his abilities has, at the time of this writing, been unable to quit smoking. Obviously, prevention is far better than cure, but we are socially sick and our social interactions need to be permeated by the breath of God's Spirit.

It is apparent, then, that as important as clean air is to our physical health, so is the Spirit to our wholesomeness. As important as it is for us all to recognize our role in the pollution of the planet's atmosphere, it is equally important for us to recognize the pollution in the spiritual arena.

Spirituality and health are major topics of discussion at places as renowned as Harvard University. Studies show that our society is at a low point of spirituality. God has been attacked on many fronts. His existence is vociferously denied by some; His involvement seriously questioned by others. Even the diversity of religions calls into question His reality. In most contexts the word "spirit" no longer references the Holy Spirit. Rather, it relates to the vigor of one's commitment or the strength of one's involvement. Only rarely does it refer to the influence of a *Person* of the Godhead.

Self-help books encourage us to find the power within, but they ignore the help from without. New Age thinking glorifies our individual selves. It's an attractive message in a society where egocentricity and egoism are all the rage. Even the well-documented tragic results—seen in our lonely, isolated, insecure, and anxious youth—don't make us join together to try to help. Society is not easily diverted from its mindless pursuit of materialism, its fixation on "stuff." Yet society is comprised of individuals, and as we as individuals let the atmosphere of heaven permeate our lives, we can, one by one, alter the headlong flight of society to its own destruction. Just as the Spirit can permeate the whole of our being, we as individuals can permeate the whole of society.

No wonder Edwin Hatch wrote,

Breathe on me, Breath of God,
Fill me with life anew,
That I may love what Thou dost love,
And do what Thou wouldst do.
Breathe on me, Breath of God,
Until my heart is pure,
Until with Thee I will one will,
To do and to endure.
Breathe on me, Breath of God,
Till I am wholly Thine,
Until this earthly part of me
Glows with Thy fire divine.
This is living praise—to glow with "fire divine."

CHAPTER 9

TEMPERANCE

Indeed the idols I have loved so long
Have done my credit in men's eye much wrong:
Have drowned my honour in a shallow cup
And sold my reputation for a song.
— *"The Rubaiyat of Omar Khayyam," Edward FitzGerald*

T Is for Temperance—the Temple of Our Purity

I used to love to sit and listen to the stories my dad would tell us children. "Daddy," we'd intone, "tell us a story of the olden days." Of course, the stories were not historical, but the recollections of his childhood days. One that stands out in my memory is the story of a runaway horse.

Of course, the era of the horse and wagon had passed when I was a child except for the occasional dray horse that might pull a milk cart. But my grandfather usually had a couple of horses he used to pull carts containing bricks and building supplies. I guess it must have been 1919 when this story took place, because Dad said he was about 6 years old and his brother John was 2.

Grandpa had been to an auction and purchased a horse, a very fine-looking animal. At least, that's the story, and Grandpa fancied himself a good judge of horseflesh. The building yard, located some distance down the road from where Dad and his family lived, had a couple of horse stables, carts, and building supplies.

Anyway, this horse looked like a nicely-proportioned animal, and on the next Sunday Grandpa suggested they try it out by taking a trip to see Uncle Jimmy, who lived six or seven miles away. Grandma—whom I only knew as elderly, because she was 40-something when Dad was born—loved to go for a ride. Dad used to say she could "ride the back wheels off a car." So Grandma and Grandpa, along with Dad and his younger brother, got into the tub trap, a two-wheeled little cart with a bench seat. Grandpa took the reins and off they set. The horse trotted out well, and then put its head down and wanted to gallop. Grandpa stood up, reined the horse's head back, and brought it back to a fast trot. Grandma, who had a fairly broad Geordie accent, said, "Bye, Faither, this horse is a ganning well."

"Aye, Jinny," said "Faither".

The horse trotted, pulling its head and straining all the way to Uncle Jimmy's, but once there, Grandpa didn't stop. He guided the horse around the circle and it ran all the way home. It pulled into the yard, hemmed in by the walls, and stood slathered in sweat, foaming at its mouth, panting in desperation. The little family dismounted from the trap. To hear my dad tell it, Grandma thought the horse was wonderful until Grandpa said, "Useless thing. It's going back to the auction tomorrow."

Apparently it had gotten the bit between its teeth, and Grandpa was as exhausted as the horse from trying to control it.

I remember asking about the bit because, having read *Black Beauty* by Anna Sewell, I knew that there were different kinds. "Oh, it was just a plain, straight bit," Dad replied. "Grandpa didn't like 'snaffle' bits and 'curb' bits that forced the horse's mouth open."

The apostle James writes how the bit and bridle are used to control a horse, but how difficult it is to control the tongue. Dad's story reminds me of how difficult it is for us, as humans, to control our emotions. So often we are like Grandpa's headstrong, runaway horse.

Of course, most of us do not think of ourselves as runaways. Most people reading this book are doing so because they are seeking ways of improving their mind, spirit, and body. But lest we get too comfortable we should recall a few Bible verses.

There are the texts that say, "All have sinned and fall short of the glory of God" (Rom. 3:23) and "There is none righteous, no not one" (Rom. 3:10). That being the human condition, we need to recognize our separateness from God—our brokenness, if you will, which means we naturally would ally ourselves with Satan were it not for the call and power of the Holy Spirit.

Paul knew from personal experience the pitfalls that await the Christian. In fact, in 1 Corinthians 10 Paul speaks of the forbears of his Jewish readers. He recounts their journey through the wilderness and the cloud that followed them, keeping them cool by day and warm by night, the water they drank from a rock. Yet none of these miraculous events could save them, and their bones littered the desert. They became complainers, idolaters, and sexually immoral. Paul reminds us that we are all subject to temptation, and in verse 12 of this chapter says,

"Therefore let him who *thinks* he stands take heed lest he *fall.*"

I remember going to answer the front door when I was about 17 years old. We lived next door to the church my father pastored so it was not surprising to see a derelict standing there. What took me by surprise was the incongruity between his appearance and his speech. A certain effluvia hung around him—the smell of old alcohol, a sickly-sweetish smell that comingled with the body odor of the unwashed. His clothes were filthy and almost greasy in appearance. His shoes were threadbare, his hair unkempt, his face covered in a ragged beard. But he spoke with a mellow, educated voice and accent.

"Forgive me," he said, "but I'm hungry." We would discover that this man had been a preacher. His wife, finding him a little socially inhibited, noticed that he relaxed after a couple of glasses of wine. Therefore, she assisted his socializing with a couple of glasses of sherry to begin an evening's entertainment. So began the decline of this man, who told my dad, "Having preached to others, I have become a castaway."

When we talk of temperance, many imagine we are living in a time warp. Surely, that was a word of the Prohibition era. We don't talk of abstinence today, only moderation. But alcohol and tobacco are not the only forms of addiction.

Our brains are made to respond to pleasure and joy and are aided in this response by endorphins that stimulate pleasure receptors. Many activities can trigger these pleasure responses. To suggest that because something triggers pleasure it must be wrong would be a travesty. Many wonderful things trigger the response of pleasure, but others carry insidious and inordinate risks.

Shopping makes many of us happy, but some are shopaholics. Chocolate has a similar effect on many of us, literally making us feel good for a while. Sex is a trigger for most, and so is food. The gambler can find the adrenaline rush, the risk, thrilling—and soon throws all caution to the wind. Even exercise can so engage a person that the exercise "high" keeps them training harder and longer. How can we actually know what we can do without the risk of falling into the trap of becoming an "—aholic"? It's very easy to become hooked.

In Carol Cannon's book *Hooked on Unhappiness* she discusses what she calls *negaholism*. Cannon lists five ways people become *negaholics*. She describes parents who "model anxiety and negativity," who "fail to demonstrate healthy boundary setting," who "abuse or neglect . . . physically and emotionally," who "sabotage . . . self-esteem by shaming unduly," or expect the child to "take second place to parental obsessions, compulsions, or addiction" (p. 49).

What is so interesting about this list is that the problems originate with one or both parents. It's reminiscent of God's saying that the sins of the fathers will be visited upon the children (Ex. 20:5), but I'm always pleased when I read the following verse. There, God says that He shows "mercy to thousands, those who love Me and keep My commandments."

Knowing, then, our innate brokenness, our human frailty, how important it becomes that we practice temperance. Let's stop and explore what we mean by the word temperance, using the alcohol abuse as an example of the need for temperance.

MORE THAN SELF-CONTROL

Most of us don't understand the meaning of true temperance. To many, temperance is self-control or moderation. One definition of temperance (stated in Webster's dictionary) is "moderation in action, thought or feeling, or moderation or abstinence from intoxicating drink." Another definition is "True temperance teaches us to dispense entirely with everything hurtful and to use judiciously that which is healthful."[1]

Temperance, therefore, means abstinence from things bad for us and moderation in things that are good. Is there any sense of moderation in the use of arsenic or strychnine? Definitely not! Some things are best totally avoided, such as tobacco, alcohol, and other dangerous addictive substances.

Alcohol.

It is estimated that up to 15 percent of people who use alcohol will become either problem drinkers or actual alcoholics. Alcohol is a chemical compound known as ethyl alcohol, or ethanol that can be consumed in a beverage. There is a common belief that wine and beer are not nearly as damaging as hard liquor and mixed drinks. However, it is the amount of ethanol, regardless of where it came from, that brings the adverse consequences. There is roughly half an ounce (15 grams) of pure ethanol in each of the following:[2]

- 1½ ounces of 80 percent proof liquor

- 5 ounces of wine

- 12 ounces of beer

The measurement of blood alcohol is expressed in milligrams (mg) per deciliter (dl) of blood.

Intoxication is correlated with the blood alcohol levels as follows:

10 mg/dl (<0.01%)	no measurable intoxication
10 mg/dl (>0.01%)	measurable intoxication
20 mg/dl (0.02%)	mellow feeling
50 mg/dl (0.05%)	social high
80 mg/dl (0.08%)	reduced coordination (legal level of intoxication)
100 mg/dl (0.10%)	noticeably impaired coordination
200 mg/dl (0.20%)	confusion
300 mg/dl (0.30%)	loss of consciousness
400 mg/dl (0.40%)	coma, death

Many people drink alcohol for what they think are its good effects: relaxation, a loss of inhibitions, and an easing of aches and pains. These good feelings are a direct result of alcohol's blocking effect on the frontal lobe of the brain—the seat of inhibition, reasoning powers, memory, and judgment. As brain messages slow down, tensions seem to float away, and a person feels relaxed. That is why alcohol is often called a social lubricant.

In the stomach the enzyme alcohol dehydrogenase breaks down 15 percent of ingested alcohol. The remaining 85 percent of the alcohol is converted in the liver. Females have less alcohol dehydrogenase than men. As a result, when a boy and a girl of the same weight are given equal amounts of alcohol, the girl will have a higher blood alcohol level than the boy. Additionally, a woman's liver is usually smaller than a man's, giving the man greater ability to deal with a given amount of alcohol. Women typically become more intoxicated than men on a given amount of alcohol.

Many parents feel that they can teach moderation, but susceptibility to alcoholism is genetic.

My wife's father perhaps knew more of the family history than he was comfortable with. He promised each of his four children $1,000 if they had not taken a drink by the age of 21. Back in the early 1960s, $1,000 was a lot of money and all four collected on the deal. The result was that two of the children have never tasted alcohol, and the other two drank only occasionally. But just a few months ago my wife contacted a cousin of whom she had lost track.

"How has life treated you?" was the general type of talk, as they looked back over some 40 years.

"Well, you probably didn't know, Janet, but I've battled alcoholism for much of my life. I've been dry now for more than 20 years, but I was really bad for many years." My wife's cousin went on to relate how her mother was a closet alcoholic all her life. She had bottles in the closets, and was seldom cold sober. She neglected her children, and became a social recluse.

Looking back in most family histories you'll usually find alcoholic ancestors. My great-grandfather, according to my dad, was an alcoholic; one of the great-grandmothers was, too. That means that my kids have genes from both sides of the family that make them at-risk for alcoholism. I know some people whose families are riddled with addiction-prone individuals. Just this week I was talking with a fine Christian who related his anxiety over some prescription pain medication he'd been given. "Before I became a Christian," he said, "I did drugs for 10 years." He had a legitimate reason to take the pain medication, but I cautioned him to discontinue them because of his known propensity.

A week later, he told me, "Wow! Am I pleased I stopped the Percocet! For five days I felt like I needed them!" He, fortunately, had destroyed them.

No wonder Paul says, "Let him who thinks he stands take heed lest he fall" (1 Cor. 10:12).

But Cannon's book says that often it is the parents who may be fashioning the children's downfall. A parent could have no greater sorrow than to see the life of a cherished son or daughter go down the pathway to destruction, having been introduced to the pathway by the parent.

When we bring alcohol into our homes, we introduce our youngsters to a potential hazard for which they have no need. The older a youth is when exposed to a drug, the less likely he or she is to become addicted. Tobacco is a classic example. Youngsters growing up in a home where cigarettes are smoked have a threefold greater chance of being a smoker. Age counts, for some 90 percent of those who start smoking before age 14 will become lifelong smokers.

Some are beguiled by their misunderstanding of scientific papers. There has been a flurry of papers suggesting alcohol may be good for the heart. Many of these studies have been called into question on the basis of warped controls and biased socioeconomic groupings. Even should the studies prove to be correct, which is doubtful, there are negative effects that far outweigh the benefits.

A recent study out of Oxford University, published in the *Journal of the National Cancer Institute*, showed that the risks of alcohol outweigh any potential heart benefits associated with moderate drinking. "These findings suggest that even low levels of drinking increase a woman's risk of developing cancer of the breast, liver, and rectum, and in smokers, cancers of the mouth and throat" (February 25, 2009, uk.reuters.com/, reported by Michael Kahn).

Paul Laner and Paul Sorlie, of the National Heart, Lung, and Blood Institute, who were not involved in the study, wrote in a commentary, "There is no level of alcohol consumption that can be considered safe" (*Ibid.*).

The study found "low to moderate consumption may account for nearly 13 percent of breast, liver, rectal, and mouth and throat cancers, with the type of alcohol consumed making no difference"(*Ibid.*).

Because the proalcohol lobby is so powerful, many don't realize the many side effects of alcohol consumption that affect the physical, emotional, and social life.

- The immune system is damaged even by the social use of alcohol in the so-called moderate drinker, increasing the risk of bacterial or viral infections:
    a. It takes only two drinks to reduce antibody production of the B-lymphocytes by 67 percent.[3]
    b. It weakens the natural killer cells, thus increasing the risk for cancers of the mouth, larynx, lung, esophagus, stomach, liver, breast, and rectum.[4]
    c. It impairs the function of the polymorphonuclear leucocyte (measurable effects are detected at 0.05% blood alcohol, the level below that of legal intoxication).[5] As the amount of alcohol ingestion rises, the ability of polymorphonuclear leucocytes to go to the infection site, as well as their ability to ingest invaders becomes progressively impaired. The more alcohol present, the greater the impairment[6]

- Gastrointestinal problems[7,8,9] (fatty liver, alcoholic hepatitis, cirrhosis, esophageal varices, pancreatitis, gastritis).

- Alcohol causes brain cells to die at an increased rate (alcoholic cerebellar degeneration and also cerebral dysfunction in the long term).

- Alcohol raises blood pressure (women seem to be more susceptible due to their relative lack of the enzyme alcohol dehydrogenase; as little as two or three drinks per day increase the risk of hypertension by 40 percent in women).[10]

- Alcohol raises the risk of stroke. (The famous Honolulu Heart Study found that even the so-called light drinkers of as little as one to 14 ounces per month have more than twice the risk of having one of the hemorrhagic strokes.)[11]

- Alcohol is clearly linked to several heart problems even though it is widely proclaimed that it is good for the heart. (The high rate of sudden death among heavy alcohol users is likely due in part to dangerous heart rhythm disturbances;[12] 20 to 30 percent of all cardiomyopathy in the U.S. is due to alcohol alone.)[13]

    1. Alcohol is the leading cause of preventable mental retardation.[14] Fetal alcohol syndrome has three major sets of problems:
    a. a tendency to lag behind in physical growth both in the womb and after birth
    b. evidence of brain involvement with such problems as intellectual impairment, hyperactivity, distractibility, and impulsiveness
    c. a characteristic set of facial abnormalities including small eye openings, a small head circumference, a thin upper lip, skin folds at the corners of their eyes, and a low nasal bridge

There are many other problems related to alcohol. These help answer the question as to whether there is a need to drink or not. The answer is a resounding no!

Government research reveals that alcohol causes more than 100,000 deaths per year in the U.S.[15] Thus among drugs, alcohol is second only to tobacco as a cause of premature deaths in this nation and is the third leading cause of death.[16]

Dr. Sydney Cohen, a drug abuse expert, described alcohol as "the most dangerous drug on earth." The direct economic and medical cost of alcoholic beverage abuse in the U.S. alone is estimated to be more than 20 billion dollars per year. Absenteeism in the U.S. government due to alcohol beverage abuse is estimated to cost in excess of half a billion dollars per year. The inestimable social cost is expressed in suffering, despair, illness, and death.

But alcohol is not the only problem. Tobacco is the world's greatest killer, accounting for more deaths than any other condition, be it cardiovascular deaths, nonsmoking-related cancer, or AIDS. The concept of tobacco as a "gateway" drug can be seen in the statistics listed below.

Between 1975 and 1986, the U.S. National Institute on Drug Abuse surveyed high school seniors to see how many of these students had experimented with illicit drugs and alcohol. The result showed a great difference between the student smokers and nonsmokers in their experimentation with mind-altering drugs:

	Smokers	Nonsmokers
Illicit drugs	95%	27%
Marijuana	94%	20%
Cocaine	49%	5%
Alcohol	18.4%	1.7%
Heavy drinking	67.9%	17.2%

This survey indicates that students who smoke are more likely to try illicit drugs compared to nonsmoking students. Tobacco is therefore called a gateway drug.

Tobacco use is a major and preventable cause of disease and premature death. It is responsible for nearly one in five deaths in the United States.[17] It accounted for an estimated 430,700 premature deaths each year from 1990 to 1994 and more than US$53 billion in direct medical costs in 1993.[18,19] It now accounts for 5 million deaths per year worldwide!

The annual medical costs of smoking constitute six to eight percent of all American personal health expenses. This figure is expected to increase to as much as 12 percent over the next few years.[20] These costs may be underestimated, since related costs associated with environmental smoke were not included. Neither were the costs of burns from tobacco-related fires, prenatal care for low-birth-weight infants of smoking mothers, nor indirect costs, such as work loss, sick days, and loss in productivity.[21]

There are more than 4,800 chemicals in tobacco smoke and at least 69 of them are carcinogenic (cancer initiator).[22] These include N-nitrosamine, polynuclear aromatic hydrocarbons, and other carcinogenic agents. There are at least 300 known poisons in tobacco smoke including nicotine, arsenic, radon, cyanide, phenol, DDT, asbestos, benzene, carbon monoxide, and formaldehyde. The three most harmful chemicals in cigarettes are nicotine, tar, and carbon monoxide.

Nicotine is a stimulant to the:
- heart (by releasing catecholamines, which increase blood pressure, heart rate, and oxygen demand)

- nervous system (It binds to and stimulates brain cells, via the central nicotinic cholinergic receptors. This effect is present within seven seconds of the first puff.)

A number of chemicals in cigarette smoke have been linked to the formation of atherosclerosis (fatty deposits in the vessel walls). The two most significant components are nicotine and carbon monoxide; nicotine damages the cells of the artery wall, allowing fatty substances from the blood to leak into the underlying tissues and start the process of atherosclerosis. This can cause various diseases and is greatly accelerated by smoking.[23]

If blockage or narrowing of blood vessels takes place, the smoker may suffer from a variety of problems: hypertension, an elevation of blood pressure; an aneurysm or bulging of the aorta (the major blood vessel transporting blood from the heart to the rest of the body); and circulatory deficiencies.

With a shortage of oxygen to the heart the smoker may experience pain, called angina. Should an artery become totally blocked, depriving the heart of blood, a portion of heart muscle will die. That's what we call a heart attack. This disease process—a shortage of oxygen to the heart eventually resulting in a heart attack—is much more frequent in smokers.

If obstruction takes place in a blood vessel of the brain, the person may suffer a stroke. It can be either ischemic (blood supply to that portion of the brain is cut off) or hemorrhagic (a blood vessel bursts, preventing a normal flow, and allowing blood to leak into an area of the brain and destroy it). Because nerves in the brain cross over to the opposite side of the body, symptoms appear on the side of the body opposite the damaged side of the brain.

Not only does carbon monoxide (CO) accelerate the development of atherosclerosis; it also has other widespread damaging effects. When the hemoglobin in the red blood cells binds with carbon monoxide, the cells' capacity to carry oxygen is diminished. All the cells in the body, including those of a fetus (when present), are relatively deprived of oxygen. The immune defenses of smokers are lowered, and they may suffer from a variety of problems ranging from influenza to cancers in sites other than the respiratory tract, cancers that would normally be eliminated by an adequately functioning immune system.

Cigarette smoking is a major cause of cancer. Thirty percent of all cancer deaths are attributable to smoking:[24]

- lung, trachea, and bronchus (90 percent)

- larynx (84 percent)

- oral cavity: lip, tongue, mouth, pharynx (92 percent)

- esophagus (78 percent)

Cigarette smoking is a contributing factor for several other cancers. In addition smoking causes many other problems:

- Headaches, which may be the result of carbon monoxide as well as decreased cerebral blood flow to the brain.

- Smokers suffer from influenza three times more than nonsmokers because of lowered immunity and inactivation of local protective mechanisms.

- Smoking causes a degree of infertility in both women and men.

- bronchitis and emphysema

- premature aging

- halitosis (foul breath) unresponsive to mouthwash and toothpaste

- gingivitis; an inflammation of the gums resulting in a three-fold greater loss of teeth than that of nonsmokers

- dental cavities—three times more common in smokers because of increased plaque, bacterial growth, and decay

A few days ago a man called me, wanting to know where in the Bible I found support for my recommendation of a vegetarian lifestyle. Others may ask, "Where does the Bible prohibit smoking?" I suppose some could ask where pornography or gambling is forbidden, too.

The Bible does not give specifics on modern problems, for there was no Internet, no casino, no tobacco known to the Israelites. However, the Bible is *very* clear that our bodies are the temples of the Holy Spirit. The fall of many a Bible character can be traced to intemperance.

I like to read the list of the fruits of the Spirit as listed in the King James Version of the Bible, for *temperance* is given as one of the fruits (Gal. 5:22, 23).

Though in other versions the word temperance is translated self-control, clearly this self-control is not of human origin but by the empowerment of the Spirit. I like to think that temperance, or self-control, comes from a relationship with God. His Spirit teaches us to be pure and guides us away from the snares and traps to which we are all too vulnerable. My friend

Peter tells of the man who wanted to lose weight, so he swore off donuts, chocolate, snacks, and ice cream. But one day as he drove to work he began thinking of his office friends and how much they enjoyed donuts and coffee. "Lord," he prayed, "I'll drive past the donut shop, and if there's parking in front I'll take it as a sign from You that I should buy donuts for the staff."

He arrived at work with a big smile and a box holding two dozen donuts. "I told the Lord that if there was an empty parking spot, I'd take it as a sign I should buy donuts for everyone," he said, "and you know what? On my eleventh trip around the block there it was!"

Self-control begins with self-knowledge, not self-delusion. How easy it is to make excuses. Sometimes it's almost laughable, the way we make excuses for our behavior. But it's very sad that the more we indulge in baser activities, the easier it is to accept them as normal.

I well remember an elderly aunt who'd always been rather finicky and very conservative. In retirement she became housebound with TV her main entertainment. I stopped by to visit one time and was amazed to see her watching rather racy, ribald smut on the TV. It was clear to me that by beholding we are changed—both for good and for worse! What seems shocking at first will become normal if we continue to view or think on it. I wonder how many of us are in danger of having such open minds that our intelligence dribbles out!

Temperance is an idea that will never be outdated, but it does refer to controlling *yourself*, not controlling others! At times I am upset to see how interested we can become in controlling others rather than ourselves. Joshua stated, "As for me *and my house,* we shall serve the Lord (Joshua 24:15)." In reality, we have such difficulty controlling ourselves, we have no business trying to control someone else. Jesus spoke of people who had planks in their own eyes, trying to remove specks from the eyes of others.

Ellen White gave great advice when she wrote, "True temperance teaches us to dispense entirely with everything hurtful, and to use judiciously that which is healthful. There are few who realize as they should how much their habits of diet have to do with their health, their character, their usefulness in this world, and their eternal destiny. . . . The body should be servant to the mind, and not the mind to the body" (*Child Guidance*, p. 398).

True temperance comes from yielding our lives to the total control of the Spirit. At its foundation, temperance is a spiritual attribute and speaks of our spirituality.

[1] Ellen G. White, *Patriarchs and Prophets*, p. 562.

[2] U.S. Dept. of Health and Human Services, "Alcohol," in the Surgeon General's *Report on Nutrition and Health*, 1988, Public Health Service DHHS (PHS) Publication Number 88-50210, p. 633.

[3] M. Aldo-Benson, et al., *Federation of American Sciences for Experimental Biology*, Annual Meeting, May 1988 (Abstract # 7966).

[4] U.S. Department of Health and Human Services, "Effects of Alcohol on Health and Body Systems," in *Eighth Special Report to the US Congress on Alcohol and Health*, National Institutes of Health (NIH) Publication No. 94-3699, Sep. 1993, pp. 177, 178.

[5] A. B. Glassman, C. E. Bennet, C. L. Randall, "Effects of ethyl alcohol on human peripheral lymphocytes," *Archives of Pathology and Laboratory Medicine*, June 1985; 109(6): pp. 540-542.

[6] R. R. MacGregor, "Alcohol and immune defense," *JAMA*, Sep. 19, 1986; 256(11): pp. 1474-1479.

[7] K. J. Isselacher, E. Braunwald, et al., editors, *Harrison's Principles of Internal Medicine*, 13th edition (CD-ROM version) (New York: McGraw Hill, Inc., Health Professions Division, 1994).

[8] W. N. Kelley, V. T. DeVita, Jr., et al., editors, *Textbook of Internal Medicine*, 2nd edition (Philadelphia: J. P. Lippencott Company, 1992).

[9] N. E. Diamant, "Disease of the Esophagus," in Kelley, et al., editors, *Textbook of Internal Medicine*, 2nd edition (Philadelphia: J. P. Lippencott Company, 1992), pp. 452-454.

[10] J. C. Witteman, W. C. Willett, et al., "Relation of moderate alcohol consumption and risk of systemic hypertention in women," *Journal of Cardiology*, Mar. 1, 1990; 65(9): pp. 633-637.

[11] R. P. Donahue, R. D. Abott, et al., "Alcohol and Hemorrhagic Stroke: The Honolulu Heart Program." *JAMA*, May 2, 1986; 255(17): pp. 2311-2314.

[12] U.S. Department of Health and Human Services, "Effects of Alcohol on Body Systems," in *Eighth Special Report to the U.S Congress on Alcohol and Health*, National Institutes of Health (NIH) Publication No. 94-3699, Sep. 1993, pp. 174, 175.

[13] *Ibid.*, p.174.

[14] *Ibid.*, Sep. 1993, p. 221.

[15] D. P. Rice, "The economic cost of alcohol abuse and alcohol dependence: 1990," *Alcohol Health & Research World*, 1993; 17(1): pp. 10, 11.

[16] J. M. McGinnes, W. H. Foege, "Actual causes of death in the United States," *JAMA*, Nov. 10, 1993; 270(18): pp. 2207-2212.

[17] *Ibid.*

[18] Centers for Disease Control and Prevention, "Smoking-attributable mortality and years of potential life lost—United States, 1984," *Morbidity and Mortality Weekly Report*, 1997; 46: pp. 444-451.

[19] V. P. Miller, C. Ernst, F. Collin, "Smoking-attributable medical care cost in the U.S.A.," *Social Science and Medicine*, 1999; 48: pp. 375-379.

[20] K. E. Warner, T. A. Hodgson, C. E. Carrol, "Medical costs of smoking in the United States: estimates, their validity, and their implications," *Tobacco Control*, 1999; 8: pp. 290-300.

[21] J. C. Bartlett, L. S. Miller, D. P. Rice, W. B. Wax, Centers for Disease Control and Prevention, "Medical-care expenditures attributable to cigarette smoking, United States, 1993," *Morbidity and Mortality* Weekly Report, 1994; 44: pp. 469-472.

[22] Centers for Disease Control and Prevention, "Tobacco Use in the U.S.A.," 2002.

[23] U.S. Preventive Service Task Force, "Counseling to Prevent Tobacco Use," in *Guide to Clinical Preventive Services* (Baltimore: Williams and Wilkens, 1996), pp. 597-609.

[24] Prevention and U.S. Department of Health and Human Services, *Reducing the Health Consequences of Smoking: 25 Years of Progress. A Report of the Surgeon General.* (Atlanta: U.S. Department of Health and Human Services, Public Health Service, Centers for Disease Control and Prevention, Center for Chronic Disease Health Promotion, Office on Smoking and Health, 1998.)

CHAPTER 10

INTEGRITY

But a smooth and steadfast mind,
Gentle thoughts and calm desires,
Hearts with equal love combined,
Kindle never-dying fires.
— *"Disdain Returned," Thomas Carew*

I Is for Integrity—Incorruptible Honesty.
"I beseech you therefore, brethren [sisters included], by the mercies of God, that you present your bodies a living sacrifice, holy, acceptable to God, which is your reasonable service. And do not be conformed to this world, but be transformed by the renewing of your mind, that you may prove what is that good and acceptable and perfect will of God" (Rom. 12:1, 2).

Here Paul succinctly outlines the wholeness with which we are to come to God. To bring our whole body as a living sacrifice, to yield our minds nonconformed to the pressures of the world so that we may prove the outworking of God's Spirit as His perfect will in our lives. Body, mind, and spirit, the whole of our existence should rise in living praise to our Maker.

In some 46 years as a physician I have seen thousands of patients. Some I have helped enormously, even saved their lives. To some I've been moderately helpful, to others perhaps useless. And to a few—by reason of unintentional ineptitude—positively harmful. Being human, I have not always been perfect in my management, but to none have I ever maliciously been hurtful or willfully done harm.

The harm that comes from ignorance is well-known to the physician, and good ones strive to keep abreast of developments in the interest of their patients.

I had one patient that I failed to diagnose. Much later she came and told me what was going on, and how she had been diagnosed by a psychiatrist.

I remember that she showed me her left forearm. She pulled up a long sleeve and I looked in amazement at the soft white skin in which was written, in scarlet raised scar tissue, the word *DIE*.

Susan (not her real name) had visited me many times, with baffling accounts and stories that had left me totally confused. She had been brought up as the only child of middle-aged parents. They were wealthy and lived very comfortable lives. Susan was quite an intelligent and accomplished young woman. She played the piano well. She was a skilled skater, reaching state-level championships. She complained, however, of multiple somatic complaints that could not be reconciled with her sheltered life nor her physical condition.

As I looked at the word *DIE*, I was amazed. "Who did this to you?" I asked. Her response was unnerving. "I did it to myself. With a cigarette."

"But you don't smoke, Susan."

"That's what I have to tell you, Doctor," she said. "I have been diagnosed with multiple personality disorder."

It made sense now. At times Susan had told me that there were blank periods in her memory. There were math tests she did not remember writing. Once, to her embarrassment, she found herself in the hospital ER after standing on a balcony railing and threatening to jump. She knew nothing of it. She told of acquiring a sexually transmitted disease, and of an abortion she'd undergone, though she had no memory of any event that could have made pregnancy possible.

"And this, Doctor, this word was written by one of my personalities."

Susan's psychiatrist was working to identify the multiple characters that made up her whole. One was a hedonistic, amoral, hard-drinking woman, fond of cursing and sleeping around. Another was the Susan I knew: studious, responsible, the height of propriety and soberness. Yet another was depressive and angry, cursing her, hurting her. It was this personality who burned *DIE* on her forearm.

Then there was an athletic, competitive, physically powerful personality, and, of course, the mathematician who got straight As in the math tests Susan didn't remember taking.

Her psychiatrist spent years working with her to bring these personalities into an integrated whole.

Eventually it was revealed that Susan had been sexually molested by her father. Not brutally, but pervasively, and she blamed her mother for her apparent ignorance of what was going on. Not able to emotionally cope with the multiple ramifications of life, her subconscious mind broke her life into compartments or personalities. Integration of the parts into a whole—or integrated oneness—took some 20 years.

Today Susan still sees her doctor, but now she functions as a single entity who can cope with the varied aspects of her life.

Such a clinical condition seems outlandishly strange, yet all of us have aspects of our personality that we tend to fit into compartments. Only when all aspects of our life are in harmonious accord, can we say that we are truly whole.

Recently I heard Pastor Randy Roberts of the Loma Linda University Seventh-day Adventist Church recount a story that is sadly typical of many of us.

While driving, a woman speeded up in hopes of making it through a traffic light before it changed to red. However, the slowpoke codger just ahead of her slowed down when he saw the yellow light, then stopped. The woman screeched to a stop behind him, and just missed rear-ending the old man's car.

Then leaning out of the driver's side window, the woman yelled and screamed at the poor man just ahead of her. Stabbing a finger toward him in a vulgar gesture, she continued to shout the abuse. She was so engrossed in these adrenalin-consuming activities that she failed to notice a police car pull up behind her. The officer walked toward her car and hearing the stream of obscenities and seeing her gesture, he ordered the startled woman to get out. "Place your hands on the roof of the car!" he demanded. The officer arrested the woman for dangerous driving and causing a public disturbance, and called for a tow truck.

Despite her protests, the woman was handcuffed, taken to the police station, and held in custody.

After a few hours elapsed the police officer came to her and apologized. "I had to run several checks on the car and your identity to ascertain you are who you purport to be," he said. "When I saw your bumper sticker that read 'Choose Civility' and saw the sign of the fish and the sticker that read 'Jesus Is the Answer,' I thought, *This car belongs to a Christian.*

"So when I saw your finger sign and heard all the obscene invective I was convinced that you had stolen this car. I'm sorry. I was mistaken."

LIFE IN DIFFERENT BOXES

Perhaps you can relate to the story. So many of us live our lives in different boxes, at different times. Most of us are not as disassociated as Susan nor as hypocritical as the woman arrested on suspicion of theft, but in reality parts of our lives have disintegrated and sometimes our actions don't show that we are followers of Christ.

Though most of us aren't merely "Sabbath Christians," yet most of us are not fully whole. No wonder the hymn writer penned "Wholly Thine, wholly Thine, this is my vow." We sense a need to be 100 percent wholly God's.

Even Paul wrote of the war that raged in his life. In Romans 7:18, 19 he writes, "For I know that in me (that is, my flesh) nothing good dwells; for to will is present with me, but how to perform what is good I do not find. For the good that I will to do, I do not do; but the evil I will not to do, that I practice."

This lack of integrity plagues us all as Christians.

As Christians we strive for transparency or honesty, but human nature is not easily trained to be honest. Very often, what keeps us in line is the likelihood of discovery. If we think we won't be detected, well, sometimes we're not totally honest.

Like the driver who bumps another car in a parking lot and looks around to see a sharp-eyed, middle-aged woman watching. He takes out his pen and a piece of paper and writes, "I'm sorry I bumped your car. I'll try not to do it again." He places the paper beneath the windshield wiper, while watching the observer drive off satisfied that he has given his name, address, and telephone number.

We may not do such a thing, but all recognize the impulse to do something like that.

Legal experts in malpractice advise doctors to be open and honest about their mistakes. Patients will forgive an honest error much more readily than they'll forgive the doctor they believe is trying to weasel out of his mistake.

Integrity leads to steadfastness or loyalty in relationships. Few hurts are as grievous as those inflicted by a friend who suddenly turned on you or by a cheating spouse. Nothing is like the pain of betrayal by someone you trusted.

But having pledged fidelity and dedication to the other, how many married people let themselves drift into an affair? Many men, like Adam in Eden, blame the seductive power of the woman. Many women excuse themselves because the man they live with "is nothing" like the man they married. But what kind of person doesn't recognize the danger signs in even the earliest of relationships? At what point did they, even subconsciously, decide to cheat?

Then sometimes the lack of integrity is blatant and even acknowledged. People mouth promises without the slightest intention of keeping them.

But integrity demands of us a sense of fairness and justice. In today's world we hear people speak of an uncommitted relationship, one of convenience or pleasure, if you will—a relationship in which both parties are free to enter relationships with others. Yet even in that supposedly open situation, there is a dishonesty to oneself. In *Hamlet* Shakespeare has Polonius say to his son, Laertes, "This above all to thine own self be true."

For some, self-deception is part of the lack of integrity—men and women willingly oblivious to the hurt they inflict on themselves and others.

Today the astounding prevalence of sexually transmitted infections is evidence of the vast changes in sexual fidelity that have taken place over the past 40 years. As a gynecologist, I was very aware that the infection rates of chlamydia were between 14 to 28 percent among groups of college women. Now human papilloma virus infection rates are higher than 50 percent in female populations of childbearing age in the United States.

Rates of HIV infection of more than 40 percent among some African populations speak to a sad lack of knowledge of the disease. But rates of HIV infection in the Washington, D.C., area have, in some instances, approached those one finds in Africa.

Surveys show that significant proportions of the North American population are concerned, aware, and on the whole careful in their sexual behavior. However, among young adults it is not uncommon to see promiscuity or—as some ingenuously prefer to call it—serial monogamy. The meaning of that term is obvious. They'll be true to that partner as long as they want to, then may change to someone else who pleases them more . . . and be true to them until—and so it goes.

Such behavior is untrue to the emotional, psychological, and biological needs for bonding. Society will be broken by this unbalanced sexual behavior that breeds infidelity in marriage.

GOD: WHOLE AND HOLY

Integrity speaks of "wholeness" for us, but God's integrity is an attribute of His "holiness."

The biblical Joseph enjoyed a favored relationship with his father. He grew up knowing he was greatly loved. He also knew and respected the God his father worshipped.

One can hardly imagine his fear and anxiety when sold to an Ishmaelite caravan and led away in bondage to Egypt. Plodding along behind camels, his future looked bleak; yet, he retained his integrity. Sold as a slave, a chattel in the hand of his master, he did not desert the principles he had learned at his father's knee.

How many opportunities must have presented themselves to him! At first, there would be the opportunity for petty theft. Perhaps to eat a piece of fruit not given to him or to pick up a fallen coin. Later he could easily have falsified bills of receipt or expense. No doubt, as the profit grew in Potiphar's coffers, Joseph's reputation grew also. Now it happens that some who are perfectionists in monetary matters and idealistic in policy or legal provisions have a weakness for things emotional. Some of us are good by normal standards, but can be spoiled or broken by our particular weakness.

How many accountants—men and women whose expertise keeps banks and businesses balanced—have fallen to the sweet lure of skimming a little off the top for themselves?

How many legislators—intelligent wordsmiths who can craft a new statute with balance and precision—have fallen to the wiles of sex?

Joseph was not to be so misled. When repeatedly accosted by a coquettish, bored wife, he backed away. Finally cornered, he asked both himself and her, "How can I do such a great sin against God?"

He recognized that his relationship with God would be compromised by an illicit relationship with his boss's wife. But today, many live such compartmentalized, fragmented lives that they will not believe that a physical or emotional affair will affect their spiritual life. Integrity or wholeness, honesty and transparency put illicit behavior in a brilliant spotlight.

Yet, integrity relates not only to the physical and emotional. Intellectual and spiritual honesty can also be tested and sorely tried. For many, doubt is viewed as a serious flaw, yet honest doubt is not necessarily a sign of infidelity. I feel sure God loves a sincere doubter and can relate to the honest of heart more than to those who doubt but pretend otherwise. "There lives more faith in honest doubt, believe me, than in half the creeds" (Alfred, Lord Tennyson, *In Memoriam*, A.H.H. 96, ll. 11-12).

A BALANCED VIEWPOINT

It is a strange anomaly in human behavior that, at times, people swing from one radical viewpoint to another. These people cannot bear to not fully understanding.

This kind of thinking is often seen in the area of health. Such people do not recognize shades of grey. To them, things are always black or white, and for many intensely so. Modification of their stance is difficult, and yet when confronted by the slightest doubt, they swing violently into the opposite camp. It is integrity that permits one to see the possibility that there might be a middle ground. The integrity of intellect often confronts the desires of emotion, the standoff between the head and the heart.

Health ministry is attractive to all kinds of people, including the more radical who want things clear-cut and pristinely defined. Recognition that science is not infallible is very important for a balanced understanding. Similarly, recognition of our internal biases, particularly in the selection of what evidence we give credence to, is another insightful attribute.

In health the evolution of scientific studies is very important. Most doctors recognize their limited capacity to analyze a study, but the general public does not let such thoughts interfere with their acceptance of evidence. Experts recommend an evidence-based approach to health, but even here problems exist in that it is not always easy to evaluate the weight of evidence.

Rational thought processes are no more secure than the evidence on which they rest. One cannot use the *number* of studies, because a whole raft of poor studies can be discarded in the light of an irrefutable one.

One cannot use the *qualifications of an author* to validate his scientific study, because great men and women can make mistakes.

Perhaps the poorest support that is amassed for a viewpoint is the *anecdotal* support. Realistically, these are arguments used in the absence of evidence.

Those who recognize such factors seldom become too radical or extreme, but many—after adopting a certain position—will listen to only arguments that support their viewpoint. In reality, they sacrifice their integrity for their belief. This type of thinking becomes even more difficult to correct when it is bolstered by a religious motivation. When beliefs are held to have been God-given, they become "irrefutable."

It is not coincidental that some of the most heinous acts in history have been committed by people who enlisted God to rationalize their actions. And the most fearsome of radicals are those who believe in their own divine authority. No appeal is heard, no quarter is given, because their minds are made up. In reality, they have denied their integrity and can become monsters in the name of God. When the argument is about an article of food or different types of exercise, the consequences are limited, but the same *absolute* convictions are analogous to the arguments that motivate terrorists who claim a God-given mandate for what they do.

True scientific thinking hears both sides of an argument, recognizes the limitations of science and the misinterpretations of dogma, and chooses a moderate response. True scientific thinking knows that absolute answers are not always available. There is truth in the statement that the simple, easy answer to a complex situation is usually wrong.

The more one knows about intracellular biochemistry, the more one recognizes the complexity of biological processes. Interestingly enough, the increased understanding does not, then, express itself in simplistic, cut-and-dried solutions, but rather yields a thoughtful approach. Why? Because integrity demands it.

Because we are finite, we have limitations. This means that even the best of us do not always understand. Job was as perfect as a person can be, yet when brought low by grief, illness, and pain he could not understand what was happening in his life. Indeed, those reading his story often do not understand and, like his three comforters, misinterpret the reality and the events that are described. Throughout the struggle, Job vainly tries to understand why almost everyone and everything important to him had been destroyed—but in all this, he does not let go of his integrity. He will not deny his core belief, his faith, and his trust. Totally committed to God, he says, "Though He slay me, yet will I trust Him" (Job 13:15).

Integrity in commitment to God protects us from so many of life's hurtful passions. Criticism, anger, anxiety, and fear often buffet the life of one who cannot yield and commit to God. The ability to make a decision or commitment even in the absence of full proof or convincing evidence is not to refute integrity. Rather, it may be a sign of one's integrity—making a commitment that requires trust. Millions commit to marriage, knowing full well that much of the future is unknown. It is not possible to know everything, but commitment says "no matter what." Such commitment protects the union; for with it eyes cease to wander and each focuses, by choice, upon what is best for the other.

Marriages built on such commitment and integrity bring security, contentment, and—interestingly—health. Persons who are supported in a marital relationship enjoy better health than do singles. Men who know that their wives love them do far better following a heart attack than those who do not have such security. Integrity in our relationships brings health to the whole person.

In Eric Harvey and Steve Ventura's little book *Walk the Talk* (Walk The Talk Company) we find a poem of possibilities. It reads:

If every person walked the talk,
Can you imagine how it would be?
A world filled with good intentions
That all become reality.

We could count on one another and
Coexist respectfully.
There would be no broken promises,
And no hypocrisy.

We'd have no problem spotting heroes,
They'd be everywhere to see.
Just by looking in the mirror, we all
Would find INTEGRITY.

Integrity provides a foundation for health.

CHAPTER 11

OPTIMISM

When it is dark enough, you can see the stars.
—*Persian proverb*

O Is for Optimism—the Celebratory Life of Faith

I have been under somewhat of a deadline while writing this book, so this morning I told my wife I'd come back from the office at noon to write the chapter on optimism. I was pecking at the computer when Lois, one of our assistants, told me she had a call from a California number, and the caller had asked me to return the call.

I did. The caller asked if I knew Erin Jacobson. I said yes, of course I knew Erin.

His parents had come to Toronto when he was just a little kid. He was full of fun and life. His curly hair and bright eyes made him a wonderful candidate for the nickname Sunshine. He had grown into a handsome man, and—like his dad, brother, and grandpa—he became a medical doctor.

He specialized in ophthalmology. He was married, and he and his wife, Amy, had three young children.

His medical practice was in Napa Valley, where he was adored by staff and patients alike. He occasionally went to Haiti to help patients there, and on these mission visits he provided medical care that would have cost thousands of dollars in the States.

"Yes, I know Erin," I said. "What do you want to know?"

The caller then told me that Erin, his wife, and their family "were killed yesterday in a plane crash."

I was dumbfounded. I was shocked. Overcome with grief. My mind went back to John and Judy, Erin's parents. Judy was a vivacious, beautiful woman, a caring mother who doted on her two young sons. John, a brilliant cardiac surgeon, driven by a need to do everything to perfection, was so proud of the boys. How could they cope with a tragedy like this?

Then we learned of the double tragedy, that Erin's sister-in-law and her husband were also on the plane, with their children. We could not imagine the heartache, the anguish—and surely some anger that will engulf these families.

In the midst of this catastrophic family disaster, my mind recoiling at the violent deaths of a family I knew and cared about—I am to think of optimism!

One just doesn't think calmly and straight at times like this. How do we cope? Where is optimism at a time like this? When so distraught, people scarcely know what they're doing. In shock, they become numb and paralyzed. Nothing seems real. After the acute phase, waves of melancholy engulf them as they face the reality, the finality of the loss. Terrorizing questions will pour through their minds. Just seeing happy photos of the children will evoke emotions difficult to manage.

So, when disaster strikes—what of optimism?

It is in crisis that our worldview becomes central to our response and adaptation.

At times like this we place our hope and trust in God. Disasters do strike, but the Christian believes that God will take anything the devil throws at us—or Him—and move mysteriously to work out some good somewhere, and for someone. We know that God takes care of the eternal issues like salvation, heaven, and restitution, but that's in the future. That doesn't impact our lives here. Yet such tragedy can draw us closer together; we can learn to support and love each other. We cherish what we have all the more, and learn to be more caring and supportive, recognizing our human frailty and vulnerability.

If we accept the words of Paul, "that all things work together for good to those who love God" (Rom. 8:28), we find that our faith bolsters optimism.

I remember sitting next to a young woman on a flight from California to Washington. She had a very friendly Seeing Eye dog at her feet. She told me, "He likes you." The dog was a Doberman pinscher, a breed we tend to think of as being fierce and aggressive, but this one licked me as gently as our miniature poodle would. As we conversed, I realized that I was seated next to a highly accomplished woman. She was a lawyer, and her visual difficulties had not done anything to stop her ambition or causes in life. She might be classified as blind, but she had more "vision" than scores of sighted people. Her enthusiasm and positive outlook on life were infectious and energizing. This young woman saw opportunity where others were gloomy. She was not going to permit a visual challenge to handicap her.

Optimism is bred of hope, not only for this life but hope in life after death. God has provided much to give thanks for, but regardless of problems here on earth, eventually we can all be winners.

Jeremiah recognized this when he wrote "Yet this I call to mind and therefore I have hope: because of the Lord's great love we are not consumed, for His compassions never fail. They are new every morning; great is your faithfulness" (Lam. 3:21-23, NIV).

We as Christians are not spared the realities of daily living that can so easily lead to despair. Life is lived by all on the same playing field, and evil befalls both believers and nonbelievers alike. It is how we respond that illuminates our faith. Having said that, we need to recognize that multiple factors can and do influence our reactions to life.

In clinical practice we see many patients who are depressed. For some, their depression is a response to events; for others, depression may indicate a chemical imbalance in their neurotransmitters. Depression is more common today than in earlier times. A sadness overwhelms one, and loss of enjoyment in previously pleasurable events clouds everyday. Fatigue drags the person down, and a sense of hopelessness, worthlessness, and a loss of meaning engulfs their entire life. They may not be able to sleep, they have unexplained aches and pains, and believing that their families would be better off without them, they may even think of ending their life.

Christians can be extremely hurtful in these situations, especially when they bring trite, unfeeling comments to the conversation. "If you had more faith, you wouldn't feel like this," some will say. Someone else: "What's wrong with you? You've got nothing to feel sad about!"

Then there was the person who asked me in all seriousness, "Should we disfellowship people who have depression?" The assumption, of course, is that if one was a true Christian they wouldn't be depressed.

We need to become agents of compassion, not judgmental Pharisees when we see people battling the aftermath of disaster with questions and despair, when we see people hopeless in their depression.

As we review the lives of some biblical characters—such stalwart men as Job, Elijah, David, and Jonah—we find depression was their experience, at one time or another. Even Jesus Himself, at times, felt sad and depressed. The Lord does not deal harshly with us during such stressful times, but leads us to a place where a clearer vision allows for optimism. Optimism is the ability to see the light at the entrance of the cave of despair. It does not mean that we are not *in* the cave, but it gives us hope to claw our way out. It is, indeed, a very bigoted person who would stigmatize some who are depressed.

The interesting thing is that we can choose to be optimistic. Many a person, battered by life, ceases to struggle. Optimism is a struggle to find the positive. It is not something we are given; it is something we decide to operate. To be optimistic does not mean we will not be down; it means we will not give in.

Paul speaks of the treasure of the gospel, and says we hold it in earthen vessels. He goes on to say:

"We are troubled on every side, yet not distressed; we are perplexed, but not in despair; persecuted, but not forsaken; cast down, but not destroyed; always bearing about in the body the dying of the Lord Jesus, that the life also of Jesus might be made manifest in our body" (2 Cor. 4:8-10, KJV).

It is indeed the focus on Jesus that brings the true perspective on life and what it means. It is so easy to become engrossed in work, worry, and activity that the more important aspects are neglected.

I have a friend who found out early in his marriage that we need to focus on what is *most* important and leave the care of *things* as secondary. His wife and my daughter were canoeing down the Zambezi River. As I look back, that seems a strange thing, for the lazy river is infested with huge hippos and ferocious crocodiles, and the shores teem with wildlife such as elephants, hyenas, lions, and Cape buffalo. Yet, in those days we were young, stupid, and bold. Just a month before we went on that vacation, a youngster had dived from his boat into the water to swim some 50 yards to the bank, and had been taken by a crocodile. His father dove in to fight the croc and though he saved his son, he lost his arm. So what we were doing, canoeing down the same strip of river, does call our sanity into question.

My daughter and my friend's wife accidentally capsized their canoe and had to cling to the slimy, wet roots of a tree while they struggled to right the heavy, waterlogged canoe. Finally, clambering into the canoe, they bailed the water out and, shaken, pale, and jittery, made their way back to camp.

The first question my friend had asked when he learned they'd capsized was not about his wife's safety but "What about the camera?" He has had to live with that mistake for the last 25 years though perhaps it was a natural thought, for he could see that his wife was clearly alive. But remembering their fear as they struggled in the water, his wife felt she needed more support and empathy than her husband showed by first asking about the camera.

We need to screen out material things, and focus on relationships. It is significance rather than success that becomes the goal of an optimist. When we see life through spectacles that focus on significance, our relationships become much more important than material things. We can be optimistic about relationships, even in situations of material distress.

In his book *Outliers* Malcolm Gladwell recounts the story of Roseto, a small town near Bangor, Pennsylvania. In 1882 the first of several waves of immigrants left their home town of Roseto Valfortore, some 100 miles south of Rome, for America and this new little Italian town thrived! Speaking Italian, close-knit families soon made it a little cocoon of Italian culture, nestling comfortably in its own warm world of friendship and camaraderie. Avoiding the fractious, often loud and strident disagreements that plagued the new immigrants from England, Ireland, and Germany, the Rosetans enjoyed a quiet and peaceful existence.

A Doctor Wolf went up to Pennsylvania for a conference, and got into a discussion with a local doctor who made a stupendous claim that flew in the face of all Wolf's experience. The year was 1950, and the doctor claimed that he rarely saw anyone in town under the age of 65 who had heart disease. Wolf, an investigator, decided to check this out. To summarize, Wolf confirmed that the citizens of Roseto actually did have less heart disease.

Of course, Wolf thought that the explanation must be their diet, but this was not the case, for these descendants of Italy had adopted the American diet. They fried their food in lard instead of the much healthier olive oil of their homeland. They ate American-style pizza, with its loads of cheese, pepperoni, ham, and sausage. Year round they ate rich sweets like biscotti and taralli—not just for special occasions. Some 42 percent of their calories came from fat! These people smoked heavily and struggled with fat tummies. They were checked for a genetic advantage, but their kinfolk living in other parts of America, with similar genetic backgrounds, did not have the health of these Rosetans. Finally, Wolf realized the advantage was not diet, climate, genetics, or exercise. Their advantage was the town itself!

Rosetans visited with each other. They stopped to spend time with each other. They had cookouts in the backyards, laughing, relaxing, enjoying each other as much as they did the steak they were eating. Wolf found three generations living together under one roof. Grandma and Grandpa were revered. They all went to church, and there were 22 civic organizations in this little town of 2,000 people. There was an egalitarian ethos, no one flaunting an advantage. If they had it, they didn't have to display it. These folk lived in a warm, protective, and supportive society. They had an optimistic, happy outlook on life. Clearly, there is more to health than just diet.

The medical community is a hard sell, and the investigational team had to work hard to dispel the skepticism—but now we know. The citizens of Roseto were doing it right.

But it's one thing to be optimistic when things look good and go well, but what about when we are sick, brokenhearted, or perhaps dying of cancer or some other oft-fatal disease? The apostle Paul prayed three times to be relieved of a physical problem, but finally came to the conclusion that Christ's grace was sufficient. He says that the Lord told him, "'My grace is sufficient for you, for My strength is made perfect in weakness.' Therefore, most gladly I will rather boast glory in my infirmities, that the power of Christ may rest upon me" (2 Corinthians 12:9).

I am not suggesting that we can laugh and be ecstatically happy all the time, but we can deliberately choose to adopt and live with a positive attitude. That is, we can be optimists.

Proverbs 17:22 tells us: "A merry heart does good, like medicine."

How true can that be? Does modern science support this proverb of Solomon, or for that matter the findings of the study on Roseto? Actually, it does. It is now well recognized that laughter is surely a powerful medicine. Let us take a few moments to see what a hearty laugh may do for our bodies:

- It exercises the lungs.

- It stimulates the circulatory system.

- It increases the oxygen intake into the lungs, which is then distributed by the blood to the cells.

- It is like internal jogging.

- The heart rate, breathing, and circulation speed up after good, hearty laughter.

- Subsequently the pulse rate and blood pressure decreases.

- The skeletal muscles may then become relaxed.

Studies show that when a person is happy and has laughed genuinely (the laughter is not forced, nor superficial), their sympathetic nervous system is stimulated, which in turn produces catecholamines, which stimulate the anterior lobe of the pituitary gland to produce endorphins.

- Endorphins are the body's *natural* opiates that soothe and relax the mind. They can relieve pain more effectively than morphine.

- Endorphins elevate the mood.

- Endorphins may increase the activity of the immune cells.

As the Bible says, laughter is surely a powerful medicine. This effect of laughter has been supported by the experience of countless numbers. We can truly be happy and have genuine laughter, especially when we have complete trust in God, knowing He is in control of our lives.

The twentieth-century lifestyle studies by Drs. Belloc and Breslow (Department of Public Health, Berkeley, California) reinforce that longevity has a close connection with how genuinely happy we are. This study involved 6,928 adult residents of Alameda County, and the results showed that those who were generally unhappy had a death rate 57 percent higher than those who were generally very happy.[1]

Of course, it's not always possible to be happy and laughing, but we can cultivate a positive attitude. Studies show that a positive optimistic attitude carries beneficial effects. Long before Dr. Fawzy launched his study showing the connection between the positive emotions and improvement in the condition of seriously ill patients, some isolated cases had suggested that positive emotions could impact one's health.

An interesting study[2] was done by Dr. David McClelland, who showed a photograph of a couple sitting on a bench by a river to a group of students. To gain greater insight into each student's subconscious perceptions and projections, he asked each to write a story about this couple. Here is what the study revealed:

- Those who wrote stories depicting the positive outlook they had of this couple, picturing them to be enjoying a happy, trusting relationship, helping each other, respecting each other, and sharing warm loving feelings with each other, demonstrated *higher levels of immune antibodies* and also reported *fewer infectious diseases* during the preceding year.

- Those who wrote stories depicting a negative outlook of this couple, in which they were seen to be manipulating, deceiving, or abandoning each other, demonstrated *lower levels of immune antibodies* and reported experiencing *significantly more illness* during the previous year.[3]

Just thinking well about others can positively impact immunity. At the same time we can see that thinking negatively about others may cause illness to oneself. No wonder Proverbs 17:22 (NKJV) continues, "A broken spirit dries the bones."

An experiment was conducted with students at Harvard University after they had taken a comprehensive personality test that measured their tolerance, confidence, and self-esteem. A blood sample was drawn from each of those students and their natural killer cells were isolated and then exposed to cancer cells for a four-hour period. The results showed:

- NK cells from students who had a healthy, positive attitude and personality destroyed more cancer cells than any other personality group.

- NK cells from students who ranked very high on the depression scale in the personality test, who were inclined to withdrawal and maladjustments and had low self-esteem, were the least active in destroying cancer cells.[4]

People who are tolerant and have a high self-esteem and confidence may be able to see the better side of every situation and consequently enjoy better health.

In the *Ministry of Healing*, page 251, Ellen White wrote:

"Nothing tends more to promote health of body and soul than does a spirit of gratitude and praise. It is a positive duty to resist melancholy, discontented thoughts and feelings—as much a duty as it is to pray. If we are heaven-bound, how can we go as a band of mourners, groaning and complaining all along the way to our Father's house?"

She also wrote, in *Counsels on Health*, page 587: "In order to have perfect health our hearts must be filled with hope and love and joy."

I remember well the family member who was a confirmed pessimist. Every ache and pain was a potential indicator of serious disease, and occasioned a visit to the doctor. This man's doctor grew weary of his hypochondria so he went to the hospital emergency department several times a week instead.

He stopped going to Florida in the winter, because he knew he'd only to have to visit the doctor while there, and he couldn't afford it!

When there was a fuel shortage, he was convinced he couldn't travel because he might not be able to get enough gas to get home.

When the economy went into recession, he talked of the Great Depression. If I suggested an outing, he didn't feel up to it. He cramped the style of all he came in contact with. His family rolled their eyes at his attitude, yet what he had was a mind-set he could have altered by choice.

Modern psychotherapy has found that deep psychoanalysis is not as effective as cognitive therapy which, though a more superficial approach, emphasizes our ability to make choices about our actions and feeling. We can be in charge of our mental health, but we have to take charge! We have to determine to be optimistic.

It is a choice we can make for ourselves.

---

[1]L. F. Berkman, S. L. Syme, "Social networks, host resistance, and mortality: a nine-year follow-up study of Alameda County residents," *American Journal of Epidemiology, Feb.* 1979; 109(2): pp. 186-204.

[2]D. C. McClelland, "Motivational factors in health and disease," *American Psychologist,* 1989, 44(4): pp. 675-683.

[3]H. Dreher, *The Immune Power Personality* (New York: Dutton Books, 1995).

[4]J. K. Kiecolt-Glaser, W. Garner, C. E. Speicher, G. Penn, and R. Vlaser, "Psychosocial Modifiers of Immunocompetence in Medical Students," *Psychosomatic Medicine,* 46 (1984).

CHAPTER 12

NUTRITION

Oh, those melons? If he's able
We're to have a feast! so nice!
One goes to the Abbot's table,
All of us get each a slice.
—*"Soliloquy of the Spanish Cloister," Robert Browning*

N Is for Nutrition—Nourishing the Soul

Every family has its old tales that kids pick up and remember. In my family we like to remember the ditties from the Tyneside area my dad sometimes sang such as "The Blaydon Races" and "Bessie Walker." When we were young he'd also tell a story from the Tyneside about a man who had a donkey. This particular man, so the children's story went, tried to train his donkey to eat less. He began by cutting the donkey's rations a little every day. Soon, it was costing hardly anything to feed the animal. Things were going great.

Then one winter evening the old codger sat in the pub, warmed by the effects of his beer, his eye rheumy and sad. Shaking his head, he said to his fellow drinkers, "I almost had him living on fresh air when he upped and died on me."

As kids, we thought that was a very funny joke, but as I have met more and more people who have an interest in nutrition, there does seem to be a group of minimalists who strive to get by on the least amount of food possible. They quote statistics of persons slightly undernourished living longer, and while there is some truth in their claims, it's a fine line between just enough and not enough.

In this chapter we'll look at the importance of feeding not only the body, but the mind, the spirit, and the social well-being of us all. In other words, nourishing the whole person. If we wish to be "living praise" we must be wholesome and complete. We seek to present ourselves, as Paul wrote, as living sacrifices.

When you study the Bible you see that food is given a primacy of place. Indeed, it is one of life's necessities. Paul mentions food in the interesting context of giving praise and glory to God, saying, "So whether you eat or drink or whatever you do, do it all for the glory of God" (1 Cor. 10:31, NIV).

We can trace the biblical history of food in many chapters of the Bible; in fact, in the first chapter of the very first book, the Bible speaks of food (Gen. 1:29, KJV): "And God said, 'Behold, I have given you every herb bearing seed, which is upon the face of all the earth, and every tree, in the which is the fruit of the tree yielding seed; to you it shall be for meat.'" It is not possible, from this single text, to be definitive about the Edenic diet, but plants clearly represent food.

After the Fall Adam and Eve were clothed in skins, which meant that animals were killed to provide the skins. Adam and Eve's son Abel became a shepherd while their son Cain became a gardener.

In the process of time both men made a sacrifice to God. You know the story. God accepted Abel's sacrifice of a lamb, but He did not accept the "fruits of the soil" that Cain brought to Him. The fat of the lamb was offered to God, a feature of sacrifice eventually made part of the ceremonial law given to Moses. Clearly, the animal had to be slain. While it is not explicitly stated, the flesh would likely have been eaten in accordance with the later practice of making a sacrifice.

Before the Flood, God directed the building of an ark as a kind of floating animal shelter. Clean beasts entered the ark in sevens, while unclean animals entered the ark in pairs of two. The laws of Leviticus regarding clean and unclean foods are clearly foreshadowed in these instructions to Noah about clean and unclean animals (Gen. 7:2, 3).

Whether the Israelites remembered these dietary laws in Egypt is not clear, but after the Exodus from Egypt, the common sense laws God gave them concerning food were recognized once again.

Yet fearing they might starve, the Israelites grumbled and bemoaned their loss of the fleshpots of Egypt. Their appetite tormented them with its craving for onions and garlic. In a wilderness, no doubt such longings were natural, but God was preparing to give them manna. For nearly 40 years they subsisted on manna, which must have been a complete food in itself.

When the Israelite spies checked out the Promised Land, they came back with reports of rich and bountiful produce. To a dusty, walk-worn, weary multitude such images must have been very tempting, but fear carried the day and Joshua and Caleb were overruled. As a result, the children of Israel struggled on for decades before entering the land God had promised to them, a land of "milk and honey."

To have food tantalizingly close, and then to have it denied, is a miserable experience. I remember Russell Staples telling of a youngster in Africa whom he teased with a plump caterpillar. He waved it in front of the little chap's eyes and watched as, in anticipation, the salivary juices began to flow. The little fellow reached out for the tasty morsel, only to have Russell move it out of reach. Finally the boy's mother said, "You'll have to give it to him now after teasing him like this!" That must be how the Promised Land seemed to the Israelites. Tantalizingly close, yet so far away.

Food became symbolic of many things in ancient times, and to this day eating with family and friends is one of our most sociable and bonding activities. Abraham kept an animal suitably fattened and ready for special occasions. When visited by three strangers on the plain of Mamre, Abraham hastily ordered the preparation of bread, butter, milk, and the veal of the fatted calf. It says, in Genesis 18:8, that the men ate while Abraham (as was the custom) respectfully stood nearby and watched. Imagine the excitement this visit brought to God's faithful couple! Clearly, Abraham recognized these men as different from the isolated nomads that occasionally drifted through. In fact, the prophetic utterances given to this aged pair caused Sarah to laugh nervously—no doubt in hope, apprehension, and disbelief. The beautiful sharing of food with strangers sought to express unrestricted generosity and the desire for friendship. Indeed, sharing a meal permitted a relationship to develop.

The Bible accords bread and wine a special status too. In fact, bread is spoken of as the staff of life, and Jesus is spoken of as the true Bread of heaven. At the Last Supper Jesus broke bread and said it represented His body and the wine represented His blood.

The historical and prophetic meaning of bread had permeated the Hebrew mind-set and culture for hundreds of years. Like a fine mist that insinuates itself through the fabric of a cloth, the concept of God as the Sustainer, Energizer, and Power for life was symbolized in bread.

Made from flour or grain meal, mixed with water or milk, and leavened with yeast, bread has been a staple of many cultures but especially those of the Middle East. The yeast, feeding on the starch of grain, formed bubbles in the dough, causing it to swell and rise like a magical living substance until it overflowed the mixing bowl. Kneading this dough, punching it down, battering it, in fact, merely spread the yeast throughout the mass. This ensured an even consistency to the bread. But "leaven," as the yeast was called, must have been viewed almost as a magical substance by those ancient, superstitious peoples. They did not comprehend a microscopic world in which yeast, tiny organisms that bud and grow with great alacrity, could thrive. The mysterious rising of bread, the ability to spread this wonderful effect by transferring a portion of the mixture to another mixture, was viewed with uncomprehending awe. The contaminating effect of yeast (though no one understood the process) was recognized as pervasive, infectious almost, and they compared it to the captivating, enticing nature of sin. Soon leaven and sin became metaphorically linked, and the bread used to symbolize the purity of God was *unleavened* bread.

In Leviticus chapter 23, we read that the Israelites were instructed to keep the Passover on the fourteenth day of the first month, and on the seventh Sabbath thereafter, which coincided with Pentecost in the New Testament. They were to "bring two loaves made of two-tenths of an ephah of fine flour, baked with yeast, as a wave offering of firstfruits to the Lord" (Lev. 23:17, NIV).

This offering represented the body of Christ, which was to be offered *with* leaven, which represents the sins of the world He bore as a sacrifice. It is interesting that the leaven was viewed as a unit, for they did not recognize the individual yeast organisms. The whole assembly was atoned for, but its each individual member played a part in the sinfulness of the nation.

The tabernacle also contained 12 loaves of unleavened bread, which were placed upon a table to indicate the presence of God within the tabernacle and later the Temple. This bread was eaten by the priests at the end of each week. Consequently, when Jesus instructed His disciples to "take, eat; this is My body which is broken for you," He was emphasizing the analogy. Take this bread and recognize that it symbolizes Me as God, a part of the Trinity; eat and recognize that you have become a priest in the body of believers. We see the church as a priesthood of believers.

Bread became the alluring call Satan used to tempt a hungry and famished Jesus in the desert. "If You are the Son of God, command that these stones become bread" (Matt. 4:3, 4); but Jesus answered, "It is written 'Man shall not live by bread alone, but by every word that proceeds from the mouth of God.'" The meaning of this interchange would be deepened for our dull understanding by John, when he wrote, "In the beginning was the Word, and the Word was with God, and the Word was God." Christ came as the Word to nurture, nourish, sustain, and save the people of this old world.

When Christ taught the disciples to pray, "Give us this day our daily bread," He was subtly telling them there is a need—not only for physical sustenance, but also a daily indwelling of the Godhead within us (Matt. 6:11). He referred to Himself as the "bread from heaven" (see John 6:32,

33), and in so doing linked Himself with the manna that fell miraculously each day, except the Sabbath, to feed the wandering, miscreant Israelites.

The Scriptures often emphasize, in figurative language, the important role of bread. Psalm 127:2 speaks of "the bread of sorrows," and Hosea 9:4, the "bread of mourners." Isaiah speaks of "the bread of adversity" (Isa. 30:20). These texts emphasize that it is by toil and sweat that our food, or bread, is obtained. The securing of food is an arduous business for some. The environment can be harsh, and competition for survival extreme. Malcolm Gladwell points out in *Outliers* that some cultures must work harder than others for their food. The Chinese wet rice farmer gets up at dawn to work all day in the rice paddy. In their culture is a saying: "No one who can rise before dawn 360 days a year fails to make his family rich." Working some 3,000 hours a year, these farmers may plant three crops a year, but their bread is surely the "bread of toil."

So, how fantastically magnificent is the free gift of God, grace that satisfies not only our spiritual need, but leads to abundant life! In Isaiah 55 God tells His children, "you who have no money, come, buy and eat"—surely the free gift of salvation.

As Jesus is the Bread of heaven, also the Word incarnate, we are spiritually fed as we study the Bible and enter into relationship with Him. Such spiritual food feeds the hungry inner soul, the spiritual and emotional needs of us all, but we cannot ignore the physical side of our wholeness.

The food we eat helps build healthy, vibrant people.

Our bodies have been ingeniously created with intricate body organs and functions. A balanced diet provides all essential nutrients for growth and maintenance of our bodies (proteins, carbohydrates, fats, vitamins, minerals, phytochemicals, fibers, and water). But a deficiency in the intake of these essentials predisposes us to disease and premature death. An excess of calories from carbohydrates, proteins, and fats may result in obesity. An excess of fat-soluble vitamins and certain minerals may cause toxicity.

Humans eat a wide variety of diets reflecting unique customs and cultures as well as availability of certain food. Some diets are superior to others, and in areas where a wide variety of foods exists, a plant-based diet has significant advantages. The food pyramids are excellent guides to our food choices, indicating the six indispensable food groups.

A plant-based diet has been demonstrated to reduce the risks of coronary heart diseases (CHD). Substantial evidence indicates that diets using non-hydrogenated unsaturated fats as the predominant form of dietary fat, foods high in omega-3 fatty acids, whole grains as the main form of carbohydrates, and an abundance of fruits and vegetables, reduce the risks of CHD. Such a diet, together with regular physical activity, the avoidance of smoking, and maintenance of a healthful weight, postpones the majority of cardiovascular diseases.[1] The NIH-funded studies of Loma Linda University support these conclusions.

The consumption of nuts and whole grain products are protective against both fatal and nonfatal Ischemic Heart Diseases (IHD).[2] Those who consume nuts more than five times a week lower their risk of CHD by 50 percent. Eating beans three or more times a week will reduce the risk of colon cancer by one half.

"There is substantial epidemiological evidence that dietary fiber and whole grains are associated with reduced risks of coronary heart disease."[3]

Vegetarians are six times more likely to eat whole grains.[4]

Vegetarians consume on average two servings or more per week of meat analogs, one and one half servings or more of nuts, and one serving or more of legumes.

It has been shown that plant foods reduce the risks of coronary heart diseases and that consumption of red meat increases its risk.[5]

Cancer rates of the colon, breast, lung, and uterus are lower in vegetarians than in nonvegetarian.

Nonvegetarians (including those eating more than one meat serving per week) were 80 percent more likely than vegetarians to develop colon cancer.

Even nonvegetarians who eat *less* than one serving of red meat and one serving of white meat per week increase their risk of colon cancer by 67 percent over vegetarians.

Nonvegetarians who eat both red and white meat more than once a week increase their risk of colon cancer 380 percent.[6]

A plant-based diet, which is high in potassium and magnesium as well as lower in salt, helps to lower blood pressure. Those who follow a plant-based diet have lower blood pressure than those who include red meats and poultry in the diet, both in the U.S.A. and Australia.[7] The amount of protein, polyunsaturated fats, and eggs did not seem to affect blood pressure. There were 13 to 15 points systolic blood pressure difference between the vegetarian and the meat-eater, and the diastolic blood pressure was six to eight points lower in the vegetarian than the meat-eater.

The prevalence of hypertension among nonvegetarian Adventists in the Adventist Health Study was more than double that of the vegetarians.

Results of several studies suggest that a plant-based diet can reduce the risk of stroke.[8] Vegetables, fruits, whole grains, and a meat-free diet are much lower in calories than the typical diet of meats, desserts, and fried foods. A 40- to 65-year-old nonvegetarian man about 5 foot 10 inches tall weighs, on average, 14 pounds more than a vegetarian counterpart; a woman was 12 pounds heavier.

It is the opinion of Dr. Fraser, the principal investigator for the Loma Linda University Study, that vegetarians may have lower disease risks because of their decreased meat consumption, but it is equally possible that this protection could be due to the increased consumption of fruits, vegetables, whole grains, and nuts.

In the first Loma Linda health study vegetarians had a body mass index of two points less than their counterparts who ate meat.

Plant-based high-fiber diets help avoid constipation and possibly diverticulosis. The best defense is a high-fiber diet of whole grains, fruits, and vegetables. Plant-based diets reduce risk of diabetes. Fruits and vegetables, whole grains, and high nutrient-density foods modulate blood sugar in contrast to high caloric-density foods. Vegetarians' reduced prevalence of diabetes may relate to the reduced obesity as a group.[9]

Comparing those who eat meat, fish, and poultry less than one time a week to those who eat it more than one time per week,[10] vegetarians have about half the diabetes of the nonvegetarian. The risk almost doubles for the nonvegetarian.

A diet high in fruits and vegetables throughout the life cycle may reduce the risk of cataracts and macular degeneration.

The consumption of low-fat dairy, dark green leafy vegetables, and "calcium-set" tofu is associated with stronger and denser bones, as well as fewer bone fractures and falls. High protein diets as found in red meats and poultry may increase risks of osteoporosis by increasing excretion of calcium.

Plant foods contain cholesterol-lowering substances, dietary fiber, phytosterols, monounsaturated fats, antioxidants, and other cholesterol-lowering substances such as tocopherols, ascorbate, carotenoids, saponins, and flavonoids.

Seven basic dietary principles have been identified.[11]

They are:

1. **Variety.** From week to week include a variety of foods from each of the six groups. The six groups are: (1) whole grains, (2) vegetables, (3) fruits, (4) dairy or dairy equivalents, (5) nuts, seeds, legumes, and vegetarian protein products, and (6) essential fats and minerals. Variety en-

sures a wide range of nutrients, phytochemicals, vitamins, and minerals required for a healthy body. Also a variety of texture and taste enhances the pleasure of eating.

2. **Proportion.** Choose the majority of foods in quantities suggested from the base of the food pyramid. This is the whole-grains and cereal section of the pyramid, plus the fruit/vegetables sections.

3. **Quality.** Choose mostly nutrient-dense foods rather than calorie-dense foods, such as desserts, candies, and sodas.

4. **Balance.** In many countries obesity poses serious health problems. A balance between energy output (exercise) and energy intake (food) will reduce obesity.

5. **Adequacy.** Both the variety and quantity of foods from each of the six food groups assures the consumption of the required constituents of the diet. These are abundant in a plant-based diet.

6. **Moderation.** Fat, sugar, and salt used in small quantities help enhance the flavor of foods and are the vehicles for fat-soluble vitamins, essential fatty acids, and certain elements and electrolytes.

7. **Avoidance.** Items of no nutritional advantage, such as alcohol, coffee, and sodas, are best avoided. Generally, refined foods, which have been processed, have had some of their nutritional elements removed.

While these scientific studies encourage us to eat a plant-based diet (meaning that the foundation of the diet rests in the vegetable kingdom) we must not think such a diet is an insurance plan against all and every disease.

No one lives forever, and even vegetarians die. They die of similar diseases to those in their culture, only at a later time in life. So dietary habits partially protect against or defer some of the consequences of life—but not all.

Much evidence is accruing that, while diet forms an important cornerstone in one's healthful lifestyle, it is only *one* component. We have, in each chapter so far, uncovered secrets of health. What a wonderful thing it is that, in "living praise" we actually sustain our health. So far, if you check the chapters, you will see that we have spelled the word CELEBRATIONS. The life of praise is indeed a celebration, an acknowledgement of God's goodness and grace in our lives. The time spent "living praise" is indeed a celebration, and it means we are contented and happy. However, it is possible to focus on detail as though the minutiae are the most important things. In the kingdom of God, there is no single winner, but a whole host of winners.

I don't know about you, but if I had ever run, swam, jumped, dived, or competed in the Olympics, I would count myself a champion. While we all know Michael Phelps has won more medals than anyone ever before, those who swam in the pool with him were also champions. Their times were perhaps a fraction of a hundredth of a second different. So too, some of the details we strain at may, conceivably, make only such minor differences in life's outcome. But that which makes all the difference is that we partake of the body of Christ, the "Bread of Heaven" It is so important that His life fills our own, that His being becomes incorporated into our own. To be truly fed, we need Jesus. To be truly kind, we must have His Spirit. It was this recognition that moved Frances Havergal to write:

"Live out Thy life within me, O Jesus, King of kings!

Be Thou Thyself the answer to all my questionings,

Live out Thy life within me, in all things have Thy way!

I, the transparent medium Thy glory to display."

Fed by the Word, attached to the True Vine, and celebrating the glory of the gift of life, we find meaning, purpose, and satisfaction. We can *taste* and see that the Lord is good; we are fed from the fountain of life, a foretaste of heaven.

---

[1] Frank Hui, Walter Willet, *JAMA,* Nov. 27, 2002, vol. 288, No. 20, pp. 25-89.

[2] Gary E. Fraser, *American Journal of Clinical Nutrition,* 1999, 70 (s), pp. 538-539.

[3] Kushi, *American Journal of Clinical Nutrition,* 1999, 70, p. 451.

[4] *Ibid.*

[5] *Ibid.*

[6] *Ibid.*

[7] Fraser, *American Journal of Clinical Nutrition,* 1999, 70.

[8] Gary E. Fraser. Diet, *Life Expectancy, and Chronic Disease,* 2003, p. 140.

[9] *Ibid.,* p. 138.

[10] Fraser, *American Journal of Clinical Nutrition,* 1999, 70, p. 535.

[11] *USDA Home & Gardens Bulletin #232,* 1995.

CHAPTER 13

SOCIAL SUPPORT

Teach me, my God and King,
In all things Thee to see,
And what I do in anything
To do it as for Thee.
—*"Teach Me, My God and King," George Herbert*

S Is for Social Support in Service—Celebrating the Tie That Binds
"By this all will know that you are My disciples, if you have love for one another" (John 13:35).

When we live a life of praise and thankfulness, we help ourselves become healthy and happy. Having an attitude of gratitude not only fosters a relationship between us and God, but also to others. Indeed, we are more blessed by the service we give to others than they are blessed by receiving it. There is more truth than we know in the words of Jesus, "It is more blessed to give than to receive."

When we do something nice for someone out of a sense of duty, our good deeds lose some of this luster and beauty. Should our hearts change—even if it is by deliberate choice—so that we actually enjoy helping others, we become increasingly satisfied with life. Adding service and support of others to the preceding 12 components of a healthful lifestyle truly makes the living of praise not only a celebration, but a series of celebrations.

Five or six weeks before I wrote this chapter, I had been in Nairobi, Kenya. My work involves me in the support of the work of others, and I was affirming the work done on behalf of African citizens infected and affected by HIV.

Part of our objectives for the Health Ministries Department is that every church should be a community health center. Naturally, such a health outreach should reflect the context of the community surrounding the church. In North America, where high-fat fast foods are a way of life, where millions spend most of their waking hours in front of a computer or TV or utilizing electronic devices, the major lifestyle diseases are diabetes, obesity, and heart disease. In addition, the major health-destroying habits are using tobacco, alcohol, and other drugs.

In such a setting, for example, the outreach for health ministry at the local church level will be different from health ministry outreach in Africa. On most of that continent nutrition is viewed not from the viewpoint of excess, but of scarcity. Infectious diseases such as diarrhea, respiratory illness, or even malaria are much more prevalent than overeating and lack of exercise. Human immunodeficiency virus (HIV) infection has also assumed monumental proportions because of patterns of migrant labor, the length of time the infection has existed in Africa, the decades when medications for HIV were inaccessible, and factors that deal with status of women, sexuality, and cultural tradition.

In such a milieu the church reaching to help its community has to have a different health agenda. So the work of the center I visited was to support those infected with or affected by HIV. Westerners do not readily comprehend the horrendous effects that this disease has had on African citizens. It is possible that sexual behaviors are fairly similar throughout many different cultures, but the attitude toward sexual behavior varies greatly.

Africa is a rather conservative continent, at least in belief. Consequently, once HIV infection gained the reputation of being a sexually transmitted disease, anyone who was HIV positive was quickly stigmatized. This is unfair. Blood transfusions and blood products were frequently used to help manage Africa's endemic malaria—which tragically helped spread HIV. Then, too, Africa was one of the last continents to stop the use of reusable needles and syringes. Also, sterilization equipment and processes were often deficient. These factors, of course, helped spread the HIV originally contracted from blood transfusions or other nonsexual sources.

Migrant laborers sent to South African mines were housed in huge hostels, holding up to 3,000 men, and their entertainment was the beer garden and its attendant females.

Trucks travel hundreds of miles, with drivers being away days on end, and again—the only fuel station in 250 kilometers becomes a major "watering hole" for humans. Such men, infected there by HIV, returning home to submissive wives who dare not ask questions, sets the stage for the epidemic we have witnessed. But, whatever the social situation, people who become infected are God's children.

With more than 50 million Africans dead of the disease, and grandparents thrust into parenting grandchildren—often several at a time—society has been brutally impacted. Some villages are sparsely populated, with children heading up households, living in the deceased parents' houses, and attending to the families' needs, while struggling to finish school.

Patients stigmatized by their families, church communities, and society in general often lose their jobs and struggle to survive.

With this background, I hope you can understand the situation and ethos of the following experience.

Next door to an Adventist church in Kenya is what has been called the HACK Center. This large house, situated on a two-and-a-half-acre plot, has been converted to a refuge and place of support for people with HIV. When I visited there I saw a display of products for sale that had been produced at the site. There were mushrooms, dried and packaged. Jars of dark honey covered another table. It was being sold for $1.50 a jar, so I bought six jars. In what I assume was the kitchen, people baked small cakes, cookies, and breads in a huge wood-burning oven. The produce was then loaded onto trays that attached to the back of bicycles, and the salesmen sold the different products in the surrounding area.

The demand was greater than the supply, and the supply was limited by the radius of the bicycles, because they could travel only so far. Clearly, they needed to take the next step—get some small motorcycles so they could travel farther. But if they had the motorcycles, they'd need another oven so they could produce more baked goods. The operation was not making money in the sense of profit, but it provided all involved with a single and adequate income.

After seeing the house, we visited the backyard. Here I saw the windowless mud-and-wattle hut in which they grew the mushrooms. Again, this provided the attendant and salesman with an income. Next to this was a poultry project for eggs; next to it, a goat project for goats' milk. Each of these projects had a little sign that said: "Supported by AAIM" (Adventist AIDS International Ministry).

A little farther around in the yard was a pottery unit, making efficient wood/charcoal-burning stoves. Yet farther on people were weaving baskets. A couple of Styrofoam-stuffed cushions were placed in each basket to hold and continue the cooking of food once the pot had been brought to a boil. The basket weavers also made shopping baskets, fruit bowls, and decorative holders. Then there were the beehives behind a hedge—some six of them. "Don't go too close to them!" we were warned. "The bees are agitated by so many people." In the front yard were the gardens. The gardener showed with pride the drip irrigation system that cost $40 for about a 20- by 20-foot garden, which was neatly weeded and growing hopeful young plants.

Besides these activities, we were introduced to some 35 children. These were wards of the township, and, as orphans, received one meal per day at the center. It did not take too long to give away half a dozen honey pots. The children sidled up to me and, with huge brown eyes, examined me. Several stroked my hairy forearms in obvious wonderment at the peculiar hair I grew. As the time for the visit drew to a close, a 9-year-old boy looked at me and held my hand. "I like you," he said.

"I like you, too," I replied.

"Take me with you to America, please."

The request was heart-rending, for this little lad had so little, and in his eyes I had so much to offer. He didn't understand the enormity of the problem that mitigated against such an action. Obviously, he didn't realize that I am closer to 70 years old than to 60, and have responsibilities to my own children and grandchildren. But I raised the question, seriously, with my wife nonetheless when I returned home.

In a Masai village we visited on the same trip I saw a church which had decided to become a community health center. They, too, had a bakery, did beadwork, and also offered a barber service. They had been operating for two years. I asked about church membership. The local pastor told me it has tripled since they had started this program of being a community health center.

Such benefits are certainly very encouraging, but what evidence is there that service actually promotes health? It is fine to be helpful, but why do we list service and social support as a health-promoting activity? Well, there are good reasons for doing so.

First, service breaks down the barriers we erect to separate ourselves from others. We so often want to live within our religious community, our own socioeconomic group, our own ethnic type. Go to a cafeteria, and see how often the different ethnic groups are eating together as a clan. Of course, we tend to sit, eat, and visit with people we know. We're comfortable within our own group, but such behavior isolates us and others. Such behavior permits the growth of those group dynamics that lead to bigotry and exclusivity.

We need to face the reality that humankind is one family. We need social support as well as a willingness to provide such service to others. We are social beings. Selfishness and pride separate nations, kingdoms, tribes, communities, and families. Selfish interests drive wedges between us. Religion teaches us that all nations are one in the eyes of God. There is unity in the family of humankind. Regardless of the color of our skin, we are all of one family by creation, and we need to have compassionate attitudes to others in our society and a willingness to provide service to one another.

One may ask, "Why is support and willingness to provide service to others so vital to our daily living?" It's a good question. The psychologist Abraham Maslow observed that love is as essential to the growth of a human being as are vitamins, minerals, and protein. There are four specific areas where support and service are extremely important.

1. The home: The relationships in a peaceful, happy house set a foundation for personal, family, community, and national well-being. "In the National Longitudinal Study of adolescent health (72,000 students), the most consistent finding was that a teenager's feeling of connectedness with the family unit provides the greatest feeling of security. Adolescents who feel loved by parents are less likely to be emotionally distressed or to use cigarettes, alcohol, or marijuana." Teenagers who have close relationships with their mothers are more likely to delay sexual activity than their counterparts. What Mom *says* helps to shape teen's perceptions regarding sexual matters. Adolescents, regardless of race, ethnicity, religion, family structure, or socioeconomic status, who are connected to families, parents, and schools are healthier than those who are not so connected. Many studies have shown the positive impact of social support and willingness to provide service to one another in the family.

A study conducted in the Case Western Reserve University, published in the *American Journal of Medicine*, involved 10,000 married men with no history of angina (chest pain), but with multiple risk factors such as elevated cholesterol, high blood pressure, age, diabetes, and electrocardiographic abnormalities. These men were 20 times more likely than normal to develop new angina during the ensuing five years. It is interesting to note that those who answered no to the simple question "Does your wife *show* you her love?" had twice as much angina as those who answered yes. The higher the cholesterol and blood pressure, and the greater the anxiety and stress, the more important was the love of the spouse in buffering these harmful risk factors. The researchers concluded: "The wife's love and support is an important balancing factor, which apparently reduces the risk of angina pectoris even in the presence of high-risk factors."[1]

Dr. Nancy Collins, at the University of California, Los Angeles, studied ethnically diverse, underprivileged, pregnant women to determine whether social support would improve the physical and mental outcomes of pregnancy. Those who received quality prenatal social support experienced fewer difficulties during labor, delivered healthier (as indicated by

Dr. Virginia Apgar's assessment method) and higher birth-weight babies. They also reported less maternal depression after birth.[2] In reviewing more than 144 studies, Drs. Hoffman and Hatch at Columbia University concluded that intimate social support from a partner or a family member substantially improves fetal growth. In women who feel loved and supported, stressful life events during pregnancy do not increase the risk of premature birth.[3] Social support definitely benefits both the pregnant female recipients as well as their unborn babies.

2. The school: Students are less likely to engage in drug abuse, violence, and early sexual activity when they attend schools with caring teachers and tolerant discipline policies.[4]

Dr. David C. McClelland and his colleagues studied two groups of student volunteers. One group was asked to view a 50-minutes film of Mother Teresa's loving service to the sick and dying in Calcutta's worst slum—a video specially chosen to induce a positive and caring emotional state. The other group of students was asked to view a powerful documentary film about World War II, chosen to elicit negative emotions and anger. On average those students who watched the movie of Mother Teresa had a significant increase in salivary immunoglobulin A, a protective antibody against some viruses. The group that watched the documentary film about World War II did not show any appreciable changes.[5]

3. The community: Dr. Sheldon Cohen and his colleagues at Carnegie-Mellon University and the University of Pittsburgh conducted a study to assess whether social ties (having social support and willingness to provide service to one another) helps to protect the human body against infectious disease.

Two hundred seventy-six healthy volunteers, ranging in age from 18 to 55, were given nasal drops containing *rhinovirus* (the virus that causes the common cold). Thereafter, participation in 12 types of social relationships was assessed: relationship with 1. spouse, 2. parents, 3. parents-in-law, 4. children, 5. close family members, 6. close neighbors, 7. friends, 8. fellow workers, 9. schoolmates, 10. fellow volunteers in charity or community work, 11. members of groups without religious affiliations (social, recreational, or professional), as well as 12. members of religious groups. The research revealed that those who reported only one to three types of relationships had more than four times the risk of developing a cold than those reporting six or more various types of relationships. These differences were not fully explained by antibody titers (levels), smoking, exercise, amount of sleep, alcohol, vitamin C, or other variable factors. In addition, the researchers discovered that the *diversity of relationships* was more important than the total number of people to whom they spoke. In short, those involved in mutually supportive relationship with a diversity of people, regardless of their background, increase their resistance to infection with the rhinovirus.[6]

4. The church: Social service to one another as one big family reduces at-risk behavior. The National Longitudinal Study of Adolescent Health (Add Health), published in the *Journal of the American Medical Association* in 1997, involved 90,000 teenagers and 18,000 parents across the Unites States.[7] This revealed that two vital factors protect children and youth from many *at-risk* behaviors such as sexual impropriety, violence, emotional distress, suicide attempts, and drug use:

Connectedness with God. An adolescent to whom religion and prayer are important is less likely to smoke, drink, or become involved in premarital sexual activity.

Connectedness with one another. Independent of race, ethnicity, family structure, or poverty status, adolescents who connected to their parents, to their families, and to their school community are protected from many risky behaviors such as premarital sex, violence, suicide attempts, drug use, and those related to emotional distress. "No man is an island unto himself." We all long to be accepted and connected with one another for support and encouragement. Social acceptance and support reduce the need to use drugs.

In addition to social support, a most beautiful part of this support is service. Dr. Gary Hopkins, who has worked for many years in the area of prevention, emphasizes the expanding body of literature that indicates service is one of the most protective modalities available when it comes to adolescent and youth at-risk behaviors.

It has been recognized for many years that the transmission of values is the essential ingredient when it comes to protecting young people from at-risk behavior. Values have to be incorporated by the young person if behavior is to change.

Gangs form strong relationships between members, and these relationships permit the sharing of values. Actions then follow the guidance of the values—often antisocial values that lead to harmful activity.

Most of us within church communities prefer to educate young people. Not only churches, but schools, and society at large have believed education is the best method of protecting youth. Education is essential, *but* as a stand-alone strategy it will fail! This is easily illustrated by studies that enquire into knowledge and practice. There is a well recognized dissonance between stated beliefs and a person's actions. More than 40 years ago, Dr.

Joyce Hopp, in her doctoral thesis, explored the difference between "the creed" and "the deed"—people may have a head knowledge, but not put it into practice. Young people who were sexually active were questioned about their understanding of the protective effects of condoms. More than 87 percent understood that using condoms provided some protection from sexually transmitted disease, but only 37 percent used them. Most smokers know that cigarettes are dangerous and people know that heroin and cocaine are addictive. However, such knowledge does not protect unless the individual's social relationships reinforce the information.

Relationships that are positive and supportive create channels through which values are transmitted. Young people then use these values in assessing what behaviors they will engage in. Recent studies have documented the overwhelmingly strong evidence that service reinforces and buttresses the choice to adopt socially acceptable and health-promoting practices.

It is peculiar, how obvious it seems that love will produce a good result in the behavior of others, yet how difficult it is for us to be truly loving.

If we seriously wish to enjoy and spread health, we need to move from the didactic, strictly educational format, and use social support and service as the means of health promotion. Parents must learn to give not only advice, but themselves to their children. Far fewer youngsters would get into difficulties if each one of them had at least one devoted, close, ethical, supportive adult they could trust. It is as true today as in 1912, when James Rowe and Howard E. Smith wrote the chorus:

Love lifted me!

Love lifted me!

When nothing else could help

Love lifted me!

If you are searching for health and seek to help others find it, begin and end with love. This way your life and the lives of those you meet will be full of celebrations.

---

[1] J. H. Medalie, U. Gouldbourt, "Angina pectoris among 10,000 men. II. Psychosocial and other risk factors as evidenced by a multivariate analysis of a five-year incidence study," *American Journal of Medicine,* 1976, 60(6): pp. 910-921.

[2] N. L. Collins, C. Dunkel-Schetter, M. Lobel, et al., "Social support in pregnancy: Psychosocial correlates of birth outcomes and postpartum depression," *Journal of Personality and Social Psychology,* 1993, 65: pp. 1243-1258.

[3] S. Hoffman, M. C. Hatch, "Stress, social support, and pregnancy outcome: a reassessment based on recent research," *Pediatric & Perinatal Epidemiology,* 1996, 10(4): pp. 380-405.

[4] National Longitudinal Study on Adolescent Health.

[5] D. C. McClelland, C. Kirshnit, "The effect of motivation arousal through films on salivary immunoglobulin A," Psychology and Health, 1988, 2:31-52, published in the *Microbiology and Molecular Biology Review* (vol. 62, No. 1, March 1998, pp. 71-101); provides further supportive evidence of improved oral bacterial resistance.

[6] S. Cohen, W. J. Doyle, D. P. Skoner, et al., "Social ties and susceptibility to the common cold," *JAMA,* 1997, 277: p. 1940.

[7] W. Blum, M. Rinehart, "Reducing the Risk: Connections That Make a Difference in the Lives of Youth," Division of General Pediatrics and Adolescent Health, based on the first analysis of Add Health data, "Protecting adolescents from harm: Findings from the National Longitudinal Study on Adolescent Health," *JAMA,* September 10, 1997.

APPENDIX TO CHAPTER 12

Ruby red. Of the top 20 antioxidant-containing foods, seven are red. These are strawberries, cranberries, raspberries, cherries, red grapes, beets, and red peppers. Other red fruits that have their own cancer-protective nutrients are tomatoes, watermelons, pomegranates, red papayas, and guavas.

Citron oranges and yellows. From foods of this color come vitamin C and vitamin A (carotenoids). Oranges, grapefruits, and lemons, as well as the many winter squashes and tropical papayas and mangos are in this category.

Emerald greens. This group should be at the top of everyone's list of foods. It includes vegetables such as broccoli, spinach, kale, collards, and the deep green varieties of lettuce.

Sapphire blue and amethyst purples. Blueberries top the list in this color group. Concord grapes, black currants, red currants, mulberries, raisins, plums, and blackberries—all abound in phytochemicals. Purple cabbage and eggplants represent this color group in the vegetables.

Diamond whites. Sparkling onions and garlic enhance the taste of many cuisines and contain potent cancer-fighting ingredients. Potatoes and their skins have been a major dietary resource to many people of the world. Another group of white foods that are high in calcium and vitamin B_{12} are the dairy products. People who cannot tolerate milk (i.e., lactose intolerant) often find cottage cheese or yoghurt quite acceptable. Where dairy products are unavailable or unsuitable, equivalent substitutes must be found to provide the vitamin B_{12} and calcium.

Golden browns. Foods of this color—the last group—are essential for a healthful diet. These include whole-grain oats, wheat, barley, corn, and rice. Delicious legumes, beans, peas, and lentils, as well as nuts and seeds of many kinds, enrich the diet with important nutrients.

Follow the seven principles of diet and choose from the many colorful foods available in order to significantly reduce the risk of many diseases.

READY TO MAKE A —CHANGE— FOR THE BETTER?

CELEBRATE GOOD HEALTH!

Improve your quality of life and live longer!

IT'S ALL GOOD!
International Recipes From the Ultimate Vegetarian Collection

THESE QUICK and easy international recipes are just the tool to help you meet the challenge of preparing nutritious meals in a hurry head-on. Using healthful ingredients commonly found at your local grocery store, these recipes are designed to help you quickly prepare tasty, nutritious meals. 978-0-8127-0483-9. Hardcover.

SEVEN SECRETS COOKBOOK
Healthy Cuisine Your Family Will Love

FOR 10 YEARS Neva and Jim Brackett owned and operated restaurants where they served delicious, healthful food. In this cookbook they share nearly 200 recipes and the seven secrets that make healthy food taste fabulous. 978-0-8280-1995-8. Wire-O.

HEALTH POWER
Heath By Choice, Not Chance

IT'S ALMOST NEVER TOO LATE TO improve your health significatly by making some relatively simple lifestyle changes. Hans Diehl and Aileen Ludington show step by step how many lifestyle diseases can be prevented, reversed, and even cured by changes nearly everyone can make at home. 0-8280-1865-0. Paperback.